THE
QUANTUM MECHANICS
OF MANY-BODY SYSTEMS

PURE AND APPLIED PHYSICS

A SERIES OF MONOGRAPHS AND TEXTBOOKS

CONSULTING EDITOR

H. S. W. MASSEY

University College, London, England

ACADEMIC PRESS • *New York and London*

THE
QUANTUM MECHANICS
OF MANY-BODY SYSTEMS

D. J. THOULESS

Department of Mathematical Physics
University of Birmingham
Birmingham, England

1961

ACADEMIC PRESS   New York and London

ACADEMIC PRESS INC.
111 FIFTH AVENUE
NEW YORK 3, N. Y.

United Kingdom Edition
Published by
ACADEMIC PRESS INC. (LONDON) LTD.
17 OLD QUEEN STREET, LONDON S.W. 1

Library of Congress Catalog Card Number 61-12282

PRINTED IN THE UNITED STATES OF AMERICA

Preface

This book is intended as an introduction to that field of theoretical physics known as "many-body theory." It is concerned with problems that are common to nuclear physics, atomic physics, the electron theory of metals, and to the theories of liquid helium three and four, and it describes the methods which have recently been developed to solve such problems. The aim has been to produce a unified account of the field, rather than to describe all the parallel methods that have been developed; as a result, a number of important papers are not mentioned. The main emphasis is on the theories of atomic nuclei, the electron gas, and liquid helium, and there is no discussion of molecular theory or of solid helium. The reader is expected to be familiar with the principles of nonrelativistic quantum mechanics and of statistical mechanics, but a knowledge of field theory and a detailed knowledge of nuclear and solid state physics are not assumed.

The book developed from a course of lectures given to members of the Mathematical Physics Department at the University of Birmingham, and I am grateful to my colleagues for their advice, encouragement, and criticism. I particularly wish to thank Professor G. E. Brown, Mr. L. Castillejo, Dr. G. V. Chester, Dr. V. J. Emery, Dr. J. A. Evans, Prof. R. E. Peierls, Mr. D. R. Tilley, and Dr. J. G. Valatin for their help, and Dr. R. F. Peierls and Mr. E. Canel who helped to read the proofs. I wish to acknowledge the hospitality of the University Institute for Theoretical Physics at Copenhagen, where a large part of the book was prepared, and to acknowledge my debt to Professor H. A. Bethe, who first stimulated my interest in these problems.

D. J. THOULESS

Birmingham, England
February 1961

Contents

V. LOW-LYING EXCITED STATES

VI. STATISTICAL MECHANICS AND SUPERCONDUCTIVITY THEORY

VII. PERTURBATION THEORY AT FINITE TEMPERATURES

VIII. GREEN'S FUNCTIONS AT FINITE TEMPERATURES

I. Introduction

The many-body systems which we consider in this book are met in several different physical contexts, and so the ideas presented here can be applied to problems which arise in various branches of physics. In nuclear physics, atomic physics, solid state physics, and low temperature physics the types of problem which we discuss arise frequently. It is not so obvious that they also occur in elementary particle physics, but the fact that ideas developed for the study of elementary particles have been applied to many-body problems is an indication that they do indeed occur.

We discuss only those systems for which the symmetry or antisymmetry of the wave functions with respect to interchange of the particles has a dominating influence on the properties of the system. There are, of course, other many-body systems whose properties can only be explained in terms of quantum mechanics; a gas of diatomic molecules is such a system. For such a system, quantum theory is needed only to explain the properties of the individual molecules, and the many-body problem can then be solved without further reference to quantum mechanics. The properties of the systems with which we are concerned here can only be understood in terms of the quantum theory of many-body systems. It is not possible to regard the understanding of the quantum effects and of the many-body properties as two distinct problems. With such systems, it is of the utmost importance whether the constituent particles are bosons, so that the wave function is symmetric, or fermions, so that the wave function is antisymmetric.

The best examples of this sort of system are the two isotopic forms of liquid helium. Both appear to be liquids right down to zero temperature, and this is a fact which cannot be explained by classical mechanics. There is a striking difference between the properties of the two isotopes, much greater than would be expected from the difference in mass between them. Liquid He^4 is superfluid below 2.2°K, flowing in narrow

1

tubes with no apparent viscosity, while liquid He³ behaves like a normal fluid down to 0.1°K or less. This difference is almost certainly due to the fact that the atoms of He⁴ are bosons, while the atoms of He³ are fermions.

Apart from liquid He³, there are several other examples of many-fermion systems whose properties are strongly affected by the antisymmetry of the wave functions. The electrons in an atom are fermions, but we only give a brief discussion of the theory of atomic structure. The properties of atoms and molecules are not very similar to the properties of other many-fermion systems, since the nuclei, so much heavier than the electrons, affect their structure so profoundly. Atomic nuclei are also composed of fermions—protons and neutrons—and some of the ideas used in nuclear theory are borrowed from atomic theory. It is also possible to regard certain nuclei as composed of alpha-particles, which are bosons, but this is unsatisfactory for a number of reasons, and is not much favoured. The valence electrons in a metal are also fermions, and it might be possible to produce plasmas whose properties are influenced strongly by the Pauli exclusion principle. The so-called "electron gas" serves as a model for either of these systems. There is another hypothetical system, which is a sphere of neutrons bound together by gravitational forces, but we do not consider that system in this book.†

There is no example other than He⁴ of a system of many bosons of finite mass which displays quantum properties, but there are many systems that contain zero-mass bosons at finite temperatures. Phonons can exist in almost all systems, whatever sort of molecules they are composed of. Spin-waves exist in ferromagnetic or antiferromagnetic materials. In many-fermion systems at very low temperatures, it is predicted that phonons of "zero sound" should exist.

At first sight it would seem presumptuous to make any attempt to construct a detailed theory of such systems. In the first place, the quantum mechanics of even a three-body system is poorly understood, and long calculations are necessary to get any results in this apparently simpler problem. In the second place, although the qualitative properties of a classical gas or solid are well understood, the theory of liquids is very difficult and their properties are not fully understood. The systems we have mentioned are certainly not like solids, and do not have sufficiently low densities to be like gases, so it might be thought that the theory of such systems should be even more difficult than the theory of classical liquids, and that detailed and laborious calculations

† See L. Landau and E. Lifshitz, "Statistical Physics," pp. 340–343, Addison-Wesley, Reading, Massachusetts, 1958.

should yield only fragmentary and unconvincing results. This is in part true, but there is a brighter side to the picture, and it is to this side that we will pay most attention.

It has been known for a long time that it is a good approximation to regard the electrons in an atom as independent particles moving in a potential determined by the average positions of all the other electrons as well as by the nucleus. There are two reasons for the usefulness of this approximation. One is that the Coulomb potential has a long range, so that the position of a single electron does not greatly affect the potential at a point; the potential is determined more by the state of the whole atom than by the position of any particular electron. The other reason is that the correlations between electrons produced by the exclusion principle are more important than the correlations due to the mutual repulsion of the electrons. For the same reasons, the valence electrons in a metal can be treated as identical but otherwise independent particles moving in a potential due to the ions and to the average effects of the other electrons. In both cases, this is only a first approximation, and the correlations between the electrons must be taken into account to explain some of the detailed properties of the systems. This approximation, in which the wave function of the system is approximated by an antisymmetrized product of one-particle wave functions, is known as the *independent particle model*.

It was not expected from a theoretical point of view that nucleons in a nucleus should behave in this way, since the forces between nucleons are strong and have a range comparable with the distance between nearest neighbours in a nucleus. It was expected that a nucleus should be more similar to an ordinary liquid drop than to an atom. It was therefore quite surprising when the success of the shell model and the optical model showed that an independent particle model of nuclei could explain many facts which the liquid drop model could not explain. The situation became even more puzzling when it was found that the potential between nucleons, like the potential between molecules, becomes very strongly repulsive at short distances. Much of the recent work on many-body problems has been directed towards an understanding of why the independent particle model works so well.

It would be too sanguine to say that we know the answer to this problem, but at least it is true that the situation is less puzzling than it was. It is clear that it is the exclusion principle that is largely responsible for the validity of the independent particle model, since it prevents many of the nucleon-nucleon scattering processes which could occur in the absence of other identical particles. It is also clear that the independent "particle" of the model need not be a real nucleon, but may be a nucleon surrounded by some distortion of the neighbouring nuclear matter, and this entity is known as a "quasiparticle". This idea is one that is borrowed from field theory, since there the physical particles are by no means identical with the bare particles to which the field operators refer, but each physical particle consists of a bare particle together with its associated vacuum polarization. The physical vacuum in the theory of elementary particles can be regarded as a particular example of a many-body system, because of the virtual particles which exist in it. The bare particles correspond to the physical particles of the many-body problem, and the physical particles of field theory correspond to the quasiparticles of the many-body problem. A simpler illustration of this idea occurs in the theory of ionic solutions, where an ion whose mobility is measured may consist of the simple ion surrounded by a variable number of loosely attached water molecules. We might refer to the ion and its attached molecules as a quasiparticle. This idea has also been worked out in some detail for the theory of liquid He^3.

The questions of how one should justify the independent particle model for a particular system, under what conditions the model may give a good description of a system, and of how one can make corrections to the model are not easy to answer. Most work on these questions has used perturbation theory, but this is unsatisfactory for a number of reasons, as we shall see in detail later. The main difficulty is that the higher order terms in the perturbation series have such a complicated structure that only the first two or three terms in the series can be calculated. Any conjectures on whether the series converges or not, or on how fast it converges, must be very uncertain when based on so little evidence. This uncertainty is increased by the fact that, in the physical problems we consider, the ratio of those successive terms that we can calculate is usually at best 10:1, rather than the 100:1 which occurs in electrodynamics.

Even if the second term of the series is much larger than the first, it does not necessarily mean that the initial approximation is bad, but may mean only that the wrong parameter has been chosen for the expansion. For example, if there is a strong repulsive force at very short distances, an expansion in powers of the potential has very large terms in it, whereas the leading terms of a series in powers of the scattering length may be quite small. Much of the work which we discuss is concerned with this sort of question. The great advantage of perturbation theory is that it provides a systematic method of calculation, but one is never sure what is the meaning of results obtained in this way.

The use of dispersion relations in this field has been limited, but it has led to some interesting results. It is possible, by the use of dispersion relations, to say that from some of the assumptions of the independent particle model certain other, not obviously connected, consequences follow. It is also possible to make deductions about the nature of the nucleon-nucleon potential from experimental results on large nuclei. Dispersion relations cannot necessarily answer a particular interesting question, but where they can be applied they may lead to rigourous answers.

Another line of approach is to use our knowledge of classical physics and macroscopic physics to correct some of the obvious shortcomings of the independent particle model. The independent particle model ignores some of the conservation laws which we know must hold, and certain simple "collective" excited states look quite complicated when described in terms of the independent particle model. Keeping one eye on the independent particle model and the other on the results which we know to be true it is not difficult to correct these shortcomings. Some interesting modifications of the expected results have been derived in this way. Such qualitative results are the most important successes of many-body physics, rather than the detailed quantitative calculations.

These ideas are developed in the second, third, fourth and fifth chapters of this book, and the methods are applied to the problems of nuclear structure, liquid He^3 at zero temperature, and, to a lesser extent, atomic structure. In the following three chapters we show that the same ideas can be used, with slight modifications, also for calculating the properties of systems in thermal equilibrium at finite temperatures. The expressions obtained are slightly more complicated, because of the extra variable (temperature), but there is no difference in principle. We apply these methods to the theory of the electron gas. The only new idea which is introduced here is that a quasiparticle may be a combination of a "particle" and a "hole", which is the basis of the modern theory of superconductivity. This idea is also of importance in the theory of nuclear structure, and may be applicable to He^3. Otherwise, these three chapters are meant to illuminate more fully the ideas introduced in the earlier four chapters.

The last chapter gives a brief discussion of the properties of many-boson systems. Most of the methods used for many-fermion systems can be applied to the many-boson problem, with slight modifications. The physical significance of the results is rather different, although the formalism is so similar. The very reason for the existence of quasiparticles, which is the basis of the similarity between many-fermion and many-boson systems, is different in the two cases. In a system such as liquid He⁴, a finite fraction of the particles condense in the zero-momentum state. These scatter against one another, forming pairs of particles with opposite momentum. A quasiparticle can be created either by putting a particle in a state with a particular momentum, or by removing a particle with the opposite momentum. The quasiparticle is therefore a combination of a particle and a hole, as in the theory of superconductivity. It is the particles condensed in the zero-momentum state which stabilize the quasiparticles and so make this approximation useful.

It is somewhat misleading to talk about the symmetry of the wave function dominating the properties of such systems, since the wave function which gives the lowest energy must be symmetric. It is rather the wave nature of the particles which has such a strong influence on the properties of He⁴. The properties of the low excited states *are* dominated by the symmetry requirement, since many low-lying states are forbidden by the symmetry.

Almost all the topics treated in this book are discussed in greater detail in the notes of the 1958 Summer School at Les Houches. More recent surveys of some branches of the subject were given at the 1960 conference at Utrecht on Many-Particle Problems, and these are published as a Supplement to Physica (December 1960).

II. Soluble Models

1. Introduction

Most of the many-body problems which are of physical interest are very complicated. We should like to construct a model which is both mathematically tractable, and which has sufficient resemblance to the original problem for us to expect its properties to be similar to the physical properties of the system. In many-body problems this is usually not possible, and so we have to be content with models which differ in important details from the original problem, and which can only be solved by approximate methods with little mathematical rigour. This is true both of quantum problems and purely classical problems. It is important to study those few models which can be solved exactly, although they are only distantly related to the physical systems, since they will show up some general features of many-body systems; we can be sure that the properties we find are inherent in the model, and do not come from faulty approximations.

In this chapter we consider two types of many-body system which can be treated exactly, and a third is considered in Chapter VI. The first is a system of noninteracting particles. Although this seems a trivial model, it is used as a starting-point for most theories of many-particle systems. In the theory of metals it is often unnecessary, and usually impossible, to take account of the mutual interaction of the valence electrons. The shell model of nuclei in its simplest form accounts for many of the general features of nuclear spectra, without interaction of the nucleons being considered.

The second is a system of particles interacting with harmonic forces. This is a well-known problem in classical mechanics, and the classical solution immediately gives a solution to the quantum mechanical problem. This model has properties which are very different from those of physical systems of interest, but it has been studied by nuclear physicists to reveal some of the defects of the shell model.

7

2. Noninteracting fermions and bosons

The Hamiltonian for a number of noninteracting particles is the sum of the Hamiltonians for the individual particles, and so a product of the individual particle eigenfunctions is an eigenfunction of the total Hamiltonian, with eigenvalue equal to the sum of the individual eigenvalues. If the particles are identical, there will generally be very high degeneracy, which is partially removed by the condition that the wave function must be totally symmetric or totally antisymmetric with respect to interchange of the particles. For bosons, the wave function is symmetrized, and is equal to

$$\Psi(r_1, r_2, \cdots, r_N) = \sum_P \psi_{a_1}(r_1)\psi_{a_2}(r_2) \cdots \psi_{a_N}(r_N). \qquad (2.1)$$

The $\psi_{a_i}(r_j)$ are eigenfunctions of the single-particle Hamiltonian with eigenvalue ϵ_{a_i}, and the summation denotes a sum over all permutations of the suffixes a_i. The wave function for N fermions is

$$\Psi(r_1, r_2, \cdots, r_N) = (N!)^{-1/2} \det \psi_{a_i}(r_j), \qquad (2.2)$$

where the suffixes i and j go from 1 to N. Both these wave functions have eigenvalue

$$E = \sum_{i=1}^{N} \epsilon_{a_i}, \qquad (2.3)$$

but Eq. (2.1) is not normalized, whereas Eq. (2.2) is normalized to unity if all the ψ_{a_i} are orthogonal to one another. Where there is risk of confusion, we refer to the single-particle states ψ as *levels*, and to the N-particle states (2.1) or (2.2) as *configurations*.

If we are concerned with a system of N interacting particles, we may write the wave function of the system as a linear combination of wave functions of the type (2.1) or (2.2), using a complete set of single-particle wave functions. Even if interactions between the particles can be neglected, it may be necessary to take a linear combination of degenerate configurations in order to satisfy some invariance principle. The best known example of this arises both in nuclear and atomic physics, where we know the Hamiltonian is invariant under rotations. Although the single-particle wave functions may be eigenfunctions of angular momentum, a determinant of such wave functions will not generally be an eigenfunction of angular momentum. Powerful methods have been developed for constructing a suitable linear combination, but the expression obtained is often very complicated.†

† See L. Landau and E. Lifshitz, "Quantum Mechanics," pp. 78–106, Addison-Wesley, Reading, Massachusetts, 1958.

Representation of a two- or three-fermion wave function by means of a combination of determinants is often convenient, and this notation is used in atomic and molecular physics or nuclear physics when only a few particles play an active part. It is a very cumbrous notation for problems in which several particles are actively involved, and we shall generally avoid it by using the "second quantization" described in the next section. Another method of avoiding its use is by the introduction of "density matrices", which, in the general form discussed by Löwdin (1955), give a complete description of a system.

3. Second quantization

If we have a complete set of single-particle wave functions ψ_i with energies ϵ_i, the $N \times N$ determinants we can form from these are a complete set for the N-fermion system, and this is the basis of the representation we shall generally use. A particular determinant can be specified, apart from a factor ± 1, by saying which of the functions ψ_i are included in the determinant. If the function ψ_i is included, we say that the level i is *occupied*, and if the function ψ_i is not included, we say that the level i is *unoccupied*. The factor ± 1 is determined by assigning a definite order to the complete set of levels. The determinant is given a positive sign if the occupied levels come in the right order as we go down a column.

Most operators with which we are concerned have a simple form in this representation. For example, the Hamiltonian H_0 is diagonal, and has matrix elements given by Eq. (2.3). It can therefore be completely determined by the values of the set of numbers ϵ_i instead of by its matrix elements. Also, there is a close relation between the Hamiltonian for N particles, and the Hamiltonian for some other number of particles, since both are defined by the same set of single-particle energies. The same is true of some other operators, such as the linear momentum

$$P_x = -i\hbar\left(\frac{\partial}{\partial x_1} + \frac{\partial}{\partial x_2} + \cdots + \frac{\partial}{\partial x_N}\right), \qquad (2.4)$$

or the angular momentum

$$L_x = -i\hbar\left(y_1\frac{\partial}{\partial z_1} - z_1\frac{\partial}{\partial y_1} + y_2\frac{\partial}{\partial z_2} - \cdots + y_N\frac{\partial}{\partial z_N} - z_N\frac{\partial}{\partial y_N}\right), \quad (2.5)$$

since the matrix elements of such operators, which we call *single-particle operators*, can be completely specified by a matrix (generally nondiagonal) in one-particle space.

Many important operators are *two-particle operators*, which are defined by matrices in two-particle space. An example is the Coulomb interaction, which has the form

$$V = \sum_{i=1}^{N-1} \sum_{j=i+1}^{N} e^2 [(x_i - x_j)^2 + (y_i - y_j)^2 + (z_i - z_j)^2]^{-1/2} \quad (2.6)$$

for N particles, each with charge e. Operators which must be defined in the space of three or more particles are not commonly needed.

Second quantization is a notation which allows us to express these operators in terms of matrices in one- or two-particle space, multiplied by operators which are defined in many-particle space. The only operators we need are the creation and annihilation operators. The *annihilation operator* a_i has matrix elements in many-particle space equal to ± 1 if the determinant representing the configuration to the right of the operator (the initial state) has the level i occupied, while the determinant representing the configuration to its left (the final state) is just the same except that the row with ψ_i in it is missing, and one column is missing. The sign is negative if ψ_i is in the second, fourth, or any even row, and is positive if ψ_i is in the first, third, or any odd row of the initial determinant. All other matrix elements are zero. For example, some matrix elements of the operator a_2 are

$$\left(\psi_1(\mathbf{r}_1,\ \sigma_1),\ a_2 \frac{1}{\sqrt{2}} \begin{vmatrix} \psi_1(\mathbf{r}_1,\ \sigma_1) & \psi_1(\mathbf{r}_2,\ \sigma_2) \\ \psi_2(\mathbf{r}_1,\ \sigma_1) & \psi_2(\mathbf{r}_2,\ \sigma_2) \end{vmatrix} \right) = -1,$$

$$\left(\psi_3(\mathbf{r}_1,\ \sigma_1),\ a_2 \frac{1}{\sqrt{2}} \begin{vmatrix} \psi_2(\mathbf{r}_1,\ \sigma_1) & \psi_2(\mathbf{r}_2,\ \sigma_2) \\ \psi_3(\mathbf{r}_1,\ \sigma_1) & \psi_3(\mathbf{r}_2,\ \sigma_2) \end{vmatrix} \right) = +1,$$

$$\left(\psi_2(\mathbf{r}_1,\ \sigma_1),\ a_2 \frac{1}{\sqrt{2}} \begin{vmatrix} \psi_1(\mathbf{r}_1,\ \sigma_1) & \psi_1(\mathbf{r}_2,\ \sigma_2) \\ \psi_2(\mathbf{r}_1,\ \sigma_1) & \psi_2(\mathbf{r}_2,\ \sigma_2) \end{vmatrix} \right) = 0. \quad (2.7)$$

The *creation operator* $a_i{}^\dagger$ is the Hermitian conjugate of a_i, and it only has nonvanishing matrix elements when the final state has one more particle than the initial state. A product of N different creation operators which operates on the vacuum (the state in which there are no particles) as initial state gives a single N-particle determinant.

It follows from the definitions that the operator

$$n_i = a_i{}^\dagger a_i \quad (2.8)$$

is diagonal, with matrix elements unity between configurations in which the level i is occupied, and zero otherwise. The operator n_i is therefore called the *number operator* for the level i. The product $a_i a_i{}^\dagger$ is also diagonal, with matrix elements equal to unity for configurations in which the level i is unoccupied, so that it must be equal to $1 - n_i$. In general, it can be seen that the creation and annihilation operators for fermions satisfy the anticommutation relations

$$\{a_i, a_j\} \equiv a_i a_j + a_j a_i = 0 = \{a_i{}^\dagger, a_j{}^\dagger\},$$

$$\{a_i, a_j{}^\dagger\} = \delta_{ij}. \tag{2.9}$$

From these relations, we can verify that $n_i{}^2 = n_i$, so that the number operator for a level i has eigenvalues 1 and 0.

If a single-particle operator has matrix elements

$$\langle \psi_i | f | \psi_j \rangle = f_{ij},$$

then in many-particle space it is

$$f = \sum_i \sum_j f_{ij} a_i{}^\dagger a_j, \tag{2.10}$$

which can be shown by comparing the matrix elements. A two-particle operator has the form

$$f = \sum_i \sum_j \sum_k \sum_l f_{ij,kl} a_j{}^\dagger a_i{}^\dagger a_k a_l, \tag{2.11}$$

where the matrix elements $f_{ij,kl}$ may be calculated without anti-symmetrizing the two-particle wave functions $\psi_i{}^*(r_1)\psi_j{}^*(r_2)$ and $\psi_k(r_1)\psi_l(r_2)$.

A very useful type of operator is

$$\psi(\mathbf{r}, \sigma) = \sum_i \psi_i(\mathbf{r}, \sigma) a_i, \tag{2.12}$$

which annihilates a particle at the point $\mathbf{r}$, with spin component σ along the z-axis. Such operators have the anticommutation relations

$$\{\psi(\mathbf{r}, \sigma), \psi(\mathbf{r}', \sigma')\} = \{\psi^\dagger(\mathbf{r}, \sigma), \psi^\dagger(\mathbf{r}', \sigma')\} = 0,$$

$$\{\psi(\mathbf{r}, \sigma), \psi^\dagger(\mathbf{r}', \sigma')\} = \sum_i \sum_j \psi_i(\mathbf{r}, \sigma)\psi_j{}^*(\mathbf{r}', \sigma') \{a_i, a_j{}^\dagger\}$$

$$= \sum_i \psi_i(\mathbf{r}, \sigma)\psi_i{}^*(\mathbf{r}', \sigma')$$

$$= \delta(\mathbf{r}-\mathbf{r}')\delta_{\sigma\sigma'}. \tag{2.13}$$

For free particles of mass M, the basis wave functions are

$$\psi_{\mathbf{k},\sigma}(\mathbf{r}, \sigma') = \mathcal{U}^{-1/2} \exp(i\mathbf{k}\cdot\mathbf{r})\delta_{\sigma\sigma'}, \tag{2.14}$$

where $\mathcal{U}$ is the volume of the system, and we are using periodic boundary conditions. We can write the Hamiltonian as

$$H_0 = \sum_{\mathbf{k}} \sum_\sigma (\hbar^2 k^2/2M) a_{\mathbf{k},\sigma}{}^\dagger a_{\mathbf{k},\sigma}. \tag{2.15}$$

The Coulomb potential for a system of charged particles is, using Eqs. (2.6), (2.11), (2.12), and (2.14),

$$V = \tfrac{1}{2} \sum_{\sigma_1} \sum_{\sigma_2} \iint (e^2/|\mathbf{r}_1 - \mathbf{r}_2|)\psi^\dagger(\mathbf{r}_2, \sigma_2)\psi^\dagger(\mathbf{r}_1, \sigma_1)\psi(\mathbf{r}_1, \sigma_1)\psi(\mathbf{r}_2, \sigma_2)\, d^3r_1 d^3r_2$$

$$= \tfrac{1}{2} \sum_{\sigma_1} \sum_{\sigma_2} \sum_{\mathbf{k}_1} \sum_{\mathbf{k}_2} \sum_{\mathbf{q}} \mathcal{V}^{-1}(4\pi e^2/q^2) a_{\mathbf{k}_1+\mathbf{q},\sigma_1}{}^\dagger a_{\mathbf{k}_2-\mathbf{q},\sigma_2}{}^\dagger a_{\mathbf{k}_2,\sigma_2} a_{\mathbf{k}_1,\sigma_1}. \qquad (2.16)$$

In the limit of large volume, we can replace a summation over momentum $\mathbf{k}$ by $\mathcal{V}(2\pi)^{-3}\int d^3k$.

A similar treatment of Bose particles is possible.[†] The annihilation operator b_i has matrix elements equal to $\sqrt{N_i}$ between configurations whose only difference is that the initial state has N_i particles in the level i and the final state has $N_i - 1$ particles in the level i. The creation operator $b_i{}^\dagger$ is its Hermitian conjugate. The number operator for the level i is $b_i{}^\dagger b_i$, and is diagonal in the product wave function representation. The operators satisfy the commutation relations

$$[b_i, b_j] \equiv b_i b_j - b_j b_i = 0 = [b_i{}^\dagger, b_j{}^\dagger],$$

$$[b_i, b_j{}^\dagger] = \delta_{ij}. \qquad (2.17)$$

4. Harmonic forces

The problem of particles which interact by forces proportional to their displacement from an equilibrium position is a standard one in classical mechanics, and can generally be solved by diagonalizing a matrix.[‡] We get a particularly simple problem if we have N identical particles of mass M with no external forces acting on them, but which interact by forces proportional to their separation from one another. The force on the particle i is then

$$\mathbf{F}_i = \sum_{j=1}^{N} K(\mathbf{r}_j - \mathbf{r}_i)$$

$$= KN(\mathbf{r}_0 - \mathbf{r}_i), \qquad (2.18)$$

where $\mathbf{r}_0$ is the centre of mass of the system. The centre of mass is therefore in free motion, while the individual particles execute simple harmonic motion about it with frequency $\sqrt{(NK/M)}$. In a three-dimensional problem, three of the normal modes have zero frequency, and $3N - 3$ have frequency $\sqrt{(NK/M)}$.

[†] See L. Landau and E. Lifshitz, "Quantum Mechanics," pp. 215–221, Addison-Wesley, Reading, Massachusetts, 1958.

[‡] H. Goldstein, "Classical Mechanics," pp. 318–338, Addison-Wesley, Reading, Massachusetts, 1950.

In principle, we can solve this problem in quantum mechanics also. A product of a plane wave for the centre of mass, and some oscillator wave function for each of the other normal coordinates is an eigenfunction of the Hamiltonian.† The difficulty is that it is not at all obvious what the symmetry of such a wave function is, so that it is not a trivial problem to find, for example, the ground state energy of a system of fermions interacting with harmonic forces. The ground state wave function of a system of N bosons is just the product of the ground state wave function for each normal coordinate, which is

$$\Psi(\mathbf{r}_1, \mathbf{r}_2, \cdots \mathbf{r}_N) = \exp\{(NKM)^{1/2}[\sum_{i=1}^{N} r_i^2 - N^{-1}(\sum_{i=1}^{N}\mathbf{r}_i)^2]/\hbar\}. \quad (2.19)$$

This gives an energy

$$E = \tfrac{1}{2}(3N - 3)\hbar(NK/M)^{1/2}. \quad (2.20)$$

It can be seen from Eq. (2.19) that, as the number of particles increases, the average distance the particles move from the centre of mass decreases like $N^{-1/4}$. For fermions the distance also decreases, but only like $N^{-1/12}$. We are interested mainly in physical systems in which the density remains roughly constant as the number of particles increases (the atom is an exception), so that this model is different in a very important respect from most physical systems. It does, however, illustrate that it is difficult to separate out the centre of mass motion, and still keep the wave function antisymmetric. Methods of solving this problem have been devised by Elliott and Skyrme (1955) and by Gartenhaus and Schwartz (1957). We shall return to this question in Chapter V, Sec. 7.

† See L. Landau and E. Lifshitz, "Quantum Mechanics," pp. 64–67, Addison-Wesley, Reading, Massachusetts, 1958.

III. Variational Methods

1. The Hartree-Fock equations

Schrödinger's variational principle in quantum mechanics tells us that the expectation value of the Hamiltonian for an arbitrary wave function must be as great as the lowest eigenvalue of the Hamiltonian.† To use this principle to determine the ground state of a system, we take a simple class of trial wave functions, and find the member of the class which gives the lowest expectation value of the Hamiltonian H. We can certainly get an upper bound to the ground state energy in this way. It is hoped that, if the trial wave functions are well chosen, the one which gives the lowest energy will have a useful resemblance to the ground state wave function.

For an N fermion system, the simplest trial wave function is a determinant

$$\Phi = (N!)^{-1/2} \det \varphi_i(\mathbf{r}_j, \sigma_j), \qquad (3.1)$$

where i and j run from 1 to N. A necessary condition for the expectation value of H to be a minimum is that it should be stationary, so that we have

$$(\delta\Phi^*, H\Phi) = 0 \qquad (3.2)$$

to first order in $\delta\Phi^*$. A first order change in Φ can be made by replacing one of the φ_i in Eq. (3.1) by $\varphi_i + \eta\varphi_k$, where φ_k is a single-particle wave function orthogonal to all the φ_j with $j \leq N$, and η is a small number. In the language introduced in the last chapter, the level i is occupied and the level k is unoccupied in Φ. The new determinant is still normalized to unity, to first order in η. The condition (3.2) is clearly equivalent to the condition that H should have no matrix elements between Φ and a determinant which differs from Φ in one row only.

† L. Landau and E. Lifshitz, "Quantum Mechanics," pp. 55–57, Addison Wesley, Massachusetts, 1958.

15

Using second quantization, we can write the change in the wave function as

$$\delta\,|\,\Phi\,\rangle \;=\; \eta a_k{}^\dagger a_i\,|\,\Phi\,\rangle. \tag{3.3}$$

If the Hamiltonian contains just the kinetic energy and a two-body interaction, we can write it as

$$H \;=\; \sum_i\sum_j T_{ij}\,a_i{}^\dagger a_j \;+\; \tfrac{1}{2}\sum_i\sum_j\sum_k\sum_l V_{ij,kl}\,a_j{}^\dagger a_i{}^\dagger a_k a_l, \tag{3.4}$$

where $V_{ij,kl} = V_{ji,lk}$. The expression on the left of Eq. (3.2) can be evaluated by using the anticommutation relations (2.9) and remembering that creation operators with suffixes less than or equal to N and annihilation operators with suffixes greater than N give zero when $|\,\Phi\,\rangle$ stands immediately to their right. The condition (3.2) becomes

$$T_{ki} + \tfrac{1}{2}\sum_{j=1}^{N}(V_{jk,ji} - V_{jk,ij} - V_{kj,ji} + V_{kj,ij}) = 0, \tag{3.5}$$

which must hold for all $k > N$, $i \leqslant N$.

We can define a single-particle operator,

$$H^{\text{s.c.}} \;=\; \sum_k\sum_i\Big[T_{ki} + \sum_{j=1}^{N}(V_{kj,ij} - V_{kj,ji})\Big]a_k{}^\dagger a_i, \tag{3.6}$$

which we call the *self-consistent* one-particle Hamiltonian. There is now no restriction on the values of k and i. Equation (3.5) tells us that the self-consistent Hamiltonian has no matrix elements between occupied levels and unoccupied levels. It is more convenient to change to the representation which diagonalizes $H^{\text{s.c.}}$, and this involves taking linear combinations of occupied levels to get the new occupied levels, and of unoccupied levels to get the new unoccupied levels. The definition of $H^{\text{s.c.}}$ is invariant under this transformation, since the sum over j in Eq. (3.6) is a trace in the subspace of occupied levels. In the new representation, we have, from Eq. (3.6),

$$T_{ki} + \sum_{j=1}^{N}(V_{kj,ij} - V_{kj,ji}) \;=\; \epsilon_i\delta_{ki}, \tag{3.7}$$

where the ϵ_i are the eigenvalues of $H^{\text{s.c.}}$. This is the usual form of the Hartree-Fock equations, and it can be interpreted as a Schrödinger equation for a particle whose potential energy is given by its interaction with all the other particles in the system.

We can interpret the eigenvalues ϵ_i as approximate excitation energies of the levels i, and call them the *self-consistent energies* of the levels.

From Eqs. (3.4) and (3.7) it can be seen that the expectation value of H in the trial ground state $|\Phi\rangle$ is

$$E_0 = \sum_{i=1}^{N} T_{ii} + \frac{1}{2}\sum_{i=1}^{N}\sum_{j=1}^{N}(V_{ij,ij} - V_{ij,ji}) = \frac{1}{2}\sum_{i=1}^{N}(T_{ii} + \epsilon_i). \quad (3.8)$$

If we evaluate the expectation value of H in the state $a_k{}^\dagger a_i |\Phi\rangle$, which is the configuration in which the particle originally in the level i has been excited to the level k, we find that it is

$$E_0 + T_{kk} - T_{ii} + \sum_{j=1,\neq i}^{N}(V_{kj,kj} - V_{kj,jk} - V_{ij,ij} + V_{ij,ji})$$

$$= E_0 + \epsilon_k - \epsilon_i - V_{ki,ki} + V_{ki,ik}. \quad (3.9)$$

If there are a large number of particles, the last two terms on the right of Eq. (3.9) are of order $1/N$, and so the excitation energy is approximately $\epsilon_k - \epsilon_i$. From this it is clear that a necessary condition for $|\Phi\rangle$ to give a minimum of the expectation value of H is that all the self-consistent energies of the occupied levels should be less than the self-consistent energies of the unoccupied levels; this condition is certainly necessary if the last two terms of Eq. (3.9) can be neglected.

2. The self-consistent field for atoms

The Hartree-Fock equations have proved particularly useful for calculating the structure of atoms. The electrons in an atom have electrostatic interactions with the nucleus, which can be regarded as a fixed charge of magnitude Ze, and with one another. Since the electron has a spin, there are also magnetic interactions, but these are comparatively small, and can be neglected in the first approximation. The Hamiltonian has the form shown in Eq. (3.4), with

$$T_{ij} = -\hbar^2(2M)^{-1}\sum_\sigma \int \varphi_i^*(\mathbf{r}, \sigma)\nabla^2\varphi_j(\mathbf{r}, \sigma)d^3r$$

$$-Ze^2\sum_\sigma \int \varphi_i^*(\mathbf{r}, \sigma)r^{-1}\varphi_j(\mathbf{r}, \sigma)d^3r,$$

$$V_{ij,kl}$$

$$= e^2\sum_\sigma\sum_{\sigma'} \iint \varphi_i^*(\mathbf{r}_1, \sigma)\varphi_j^*(\mathbf{r}_2, \sigma')|\mathbf{r}_1 - \mathbf{r}_2|^{-1}\varphi_k(\mathbf{r}_1, \sigma)\varphi_l(\mathbf{r}_2, \sigma')d^3r_1 d^3r_2.$$

$$(3.10)$$

The self-consistent field equation (3.7) can be written as

$$-\hbar^2\nabla^2\varphi_i(r,\,\sigma)/2M \, - \, Ze^2\varphi_i(\mathbf{r},\,\sigma)/r$$

$$+e^2\sum_{j=1}^{Z}\,\sum_{\sigma'}\int\varphi_j{}^*(\mathbf{r}',\,\sigma')\,|\,\mathbf{r}\,-\,\mathbf{r}'\,|^{-1}\varphi_j(\mathbf{r}',\,\sigma')d^3r'\varphi_i(\mathbf{r},\,\sigma)$$

$$-e^2\sum_{j=1}^{Z}\,\sum_{\sigma'}\int\varphi_j{}^*(\mathbf{r}',\,\sigma')\,|\,\mathbf{r}\,-\,\mathbf{r}'\,|^{-1}\varphi_j(\mathbf{r},\,\sigma)\varphi_i(\mathbf{r}',\,\sigma')d^3r' = \epsilon_i\varphi_i(\mathbf{r},\,\sigma) \quad (3.11)$$

The factor multiplying $-e\varphi_i(\mathbf{r},\,\sigma)$ in the third term on the left of Eq. (3.11) is the average Coulomb potential of all the electrons in the atom, and this was the only term taken into account in the original theory of Hartree (1928). The fourth term makes the equation for φ_i nonlocal. It has some important effects, and was introduced into the theory by Fock (1930), who derived these equations by the method used here.

Equation (3.11) gives a set of coupled nonlinear equations for the wave functions φ_i, and so it is not easy to solve directly, but an iterative method of solution has proved successful. A guess is made for the self-consistent potential, and the Schrödinger equation solved for that potential. The wave functions found are used to calculate a second approximation to the potential, and the process is repeated until self-consistency is attained. One feature which we can see from Eq. (3.11) is that at large distances from the nucleus, where the electron density is negligible, the only effect of the fourth term is to cancel the interaction of an electron with its own average potential. At very large distances the potential energy is therefore just $-e^2/r$, and so the asymptotic behaviour of wave functions is the same as the asymptotic behaviour of wave functions for a hydrogen atom. A full discussion of the use of this theory for calculating atomic wave functions is given in the book by Hartree (1957).

3. The Thomas-Fermi method

In the Hartree approximation, the fourth term on the left of Eq. (3.11), the exchange term, is neglected, and so the potential is a local function. As in classical electrostatic theory, the potential energy density is half of the Hartree potential multiplied by the charge density. We assume that all other contributions to the energy, in particular the kinetic energy, are functions only of the local particle density. This is a good approximation only if the self-consistent field varies slowly, and variations which are rapid compared with the wavelength of an electron make it a very poor approximation.

We can calculate the appropriate dependence of kinetic energy on density by assuming that the density is uniform. In this case the occupied states are all the plane wave states with momentum up to a certain limiting value $\hbar k_F$ which is known as the *Fermi momentum*. The Fermi momentum must be related to the density ρ by

$$\rho = (2\pi)^{-3} \sum_\sigma \int^{k_F} d^3k = k_F^3/3\pi^2. \tag{3.12}$$

The kinetic energy density is

$$E_K = 3\hbar^2 k_F^2 \rho/10M = 3\hbar^2 (3\pi^2)^{2/3} \rho^{5/3}/10M, \tag{3.13}$$

so that we now have the required relation between kinetic energy and density. If the system is in equilibrium, the total energy of the most energetic particle must be the same everywhere, or else the energy of the system could be reduced by moving a particle to a place with lower energy. This condition gives us the equation

$$(3\pi^2)^{2/3} \hbar^2 [\rho(\mathbf{r})]^{2/3}/2M - e\varphi(\mathbf{r}) = -e\varphi_0, \tag{3.14}$$

where $\varphi(\mathbf{r})$ is the potential at $\mathbf{r}$. We can now use Poisson's equation for the potential, which gives

$$\nabla^2\varphi(\mathbf{r}) = 4\pi e\rho(\mathbf{r})$$
$$= 4\pi e(2Me)^{3/2}[\varphi(\mathbf{r}) - \varphi_0]^{3/2}/3\pi^2\hbar^3. \tag{3.15}$$

The boundary conditions for which this equation must be solved are given by the field at the nucleus, equal to Ze/r^2 for small r, and by the way in which the density must fall off at large distances. For a neutral atom, φ_0 is zero, and, if we make the substitution

$$\varphi(r) = (Ze/r)\chi(rZ^{1/3}Me^2/\hbar^2) \tag{3.16}$$

in Eq. (3.15), we get the equation

$$\chi''(x) = (4/3\pi)x^{-1/2}\chi(x), \tag{3.17}$$

with the boundary conditions $\chi(0) = 1$ and $\chi(\infty) = 0$. All the information about a neutral atom can therefore be obtained from a table of this single function of one variable. This dimensionless equation shows that the radius of the atom must decrease like $Z^{-1/3}$ as the number of electrons increases, while the energy increases like $Z^{7/3}$. The atom is the only system we shall consider in which the energy is not roughly proportional to the total number of particles in the system.

This method gives a good picture of how the energy and size of an atom varies with atomic number, although it naturally gives none of the detailed behaviour. The solution of the Thomas-Fermi equation gives a useful starting point for an iterative solution of the Hartree-

Fock equations. The method can be refined by allowing for the exchange energy, which is treated as a function of density, and is proportional to ρ^2. Attempts have been made to allow for the effect of the nonuniformity of the field on the kinetic energy, but these are of doubtful value. A detailed discussion of the application of this method to the theory of atomic structure has been given in a book by Gombás (1949). A general survey of the method has been made by March (1957).

4. Nuclear matter

The rapidity with which the density and the energy of atoms rise with increasing atomic number makes us unable to make any useful comparisons between the properties of an atom and the properties of an extended system of fermions, such as liquid He^3 or the electrons in a metal. Although it is impossible to have an extended system of nucleons, there is a sense in which nuclei do resemble extended systems. In the *liquid drop model* of the nucleus, we picture a nucleus as containing a central region with uniform density of particles, and a surface at which the density falls away rapidly to zero.

There are now two lines of evidence which show that this is a moderately accurate picture of nuclei, and there are a number of less precise arguments which support it. The model suggests a formula for nuclear energies, known as Weizsäcker's semi-empirical mass formula, which is

$$E(N, Z) = -a_1 A + a_2 A^{2/3} + a_3 Z^2 A^{-1/3} + \tfrac{1}{4} a_4 (N - Z)^2 / A, \qquad (3.18)$$

where Z is the number of protons, N is the number of neutrons, and A is the mass number $N + Z$ (Bethe and Bacher, 1936). The first term comes from the uniform density of the nucleus. Unless a particle is near the surface of the nucleus, it will see the same surroundings wherever it is, and in whatever nucleus it is, so the energy of the particle is the same, to a first approximation. The second term is the *surface energy*; the area of the surface is proportional to $A^{2/3}$, and it is supposed that a particle in the surface has an extra energy because it has less neighbours to attract it, just as a particle in the surface of a liquid has an extra energy. The third term is the energy of a uniform charge distribution inside a sphere with radius proportional to $A^{1/3}$, and is the *Coulomb energy*. The fourth term is the *symmetry energy*, which is an energy due to the action of the exclusion principle, and has no analogue in a classical liquid. It is obvious that the exclusion principle favours equal numbers of protons and neutrons, but the quadratic form is taken for convenience, for want of anything better.

The parameters in Eq. (3.18) can be adjusted to give a good fit to the general tendencies of nuclear binding energies, although there are quite large deviations in individual cases. The most careful fit in recent years has been done by Green (1958), although there are better fits which have been made to other empirical formulae. The main deviations occur because of the pairing energy, which favours an even number of protons and of neutrons, and because of the closing of neutron or proton shells.

There is now detailed evidence on the sizes of nuclei which confirms some of the features predicted by the liquid drop model. Scattering of high energy electrons from nuclei has revealed the charge distribution in the nucleus (Hofstadter, 1956). The charge density appears to be uniform in the centre, and to fall from 0.9 to 0.1 of its maximum value over a distance of 2.5×10^{-13} cm. The central density is equal to $(\frac{4}{3}\pi r_0^3)^{-1}$ particles per unit volume, where r_0 is found to be 1.12×10^{-13} cm, if it is assumed that the neutrons are distributed over the same volume as the protons. Not all nuclei are, however, spherical.

These two lines of evidence show that nuclear forces *saturate*, and that, in the absence of the Coulomb forces which become dominant for large Z, a mixture of an equal number of protons and neutrons would be bound together to form a stable aggregate, which would have an energy proportional to the total number of particles in the limit of large A. This hypothetical system of a large number of bound protons and neutrons is what is known as *nuclear matter*; it is the Coulomb repulsion between the protons that makes such an extended system impossible to produce. The properties of the hypothetical nuclear matter can be deduced from the properties of real nuclei, so that the energy per particle is, approximately, the $-a_1$ of Eq. (3.18), and a_1 is 15.9 Mev (Green, 1958).

It is generally assumed that nuclear matter is incompressible, and the observed constancy of the central density of nuclei as the mass number is varied shows that this is true. Inside a nucleus there is a positive pressure due to the surface tension, and a negative pressure due to electrostatic repulsion, so that the total pressure is positive, but decreases with increasing atomic number. If nuclear matter were compressible, the central density would be greater for medium nuclei than for heavy nuclei. The observed constancy of the central density shows that the derivative of pressure with respect to particle density must be greater than 15 Mev per particle.

It might be supposed that the nucleus would be a suitable system for the application of the Fermi-Thomas method, since its density appears to vary quite slowly. This has been attempted in a series of papers by Gombás and his collaborators (1952a, b, 1955, 1957), but the method has not proved very successful. It would be possible to use the same method for a Yukawa potential as was used for a Coulomb potential, but no monotonic local potential like this gives saturation.† With exchange potentials, which can give saturation, it is easy to write down the energy as a function of density, but it is not easy to see what to do about the effect of density variation on the potential energy. Gombás ignores this effect, and only takes account of the effects of density variation on the Coulomb energy and the kinetic energy (he uses a correction for the kinetic energy which is probably incorrect). The calculated density varies much too smoothly, and the variation is close to Gaussian in form; this is very different from the observed density, which falls off quite rapidly at the nuclear surface. An attempt has been made by Swiatecki (1951) to improve the treatment of the surface region, but his method only deals with the kinetic energy, not with the potential energy. Critical discussions of the problem of calculating the properties of the nuclear surface have been given by Swiatecki (1957) and by Wilets (1958).

5. The Hartree-Fock equations for extended systems

Attempts to calculate the properties of the nuclear surface have not been successful, but it should be a much simpler task to calculate the bulk energy and equilibrium density of nuclear matter. For an extended system such as nuclear matter the Hartree-Fock equations have a particularly simple solution. In the absence of any external field, both T and V of Eq. (3.4) conserve momentum, and so the plane wave representation (2.14) diagonalizes both T_{ki} and $V_{kj,ij}$ of Eq. (3.7). The plane wave representation therefore satisfies the Hartree-Fock equations (3.7), and the self-consistent energies are

$$\epsilon_i = T_{ii} + \sum_j (V_{ij,ij} - V_{ij,ji}), \tag{3.19}$$

where the sum over j goes over all states with momenta less than the Fermi momentum. This is the significance of the statement that, for an extended system, the self-consistency problem is trivial (Bethe, 1956). If V is a local potential, the matrix element depends only on the momentum transfer, and so $V_{ij,ij}$ is constant, but the exchange part $V_{ij,ji}$ depends on i. The Hartree-Fock potential therefore depends on i, and, if we transform back from momentum representation to configuration space representation, the potential is nonlocal, as it is in Eq. (3.11). A local one-particle potential, diagonal in momentum representation, merely shifts all energy levels by the same amount.

In each plane wave state with a particular momentum **k** it is possible

† See H. A. Bethe and P. Morrison, "Elementary Nuclear Theory," Wiley, New York, 1956, pp. 108–118, for a discussion of the problem of saturation.

to have a neutron and a proton with spin up and with spin down. There are therefore four states for each momentum, which can be specified by giving the charge state (proton or neutron) and the spin direction (up or down). In order to avoid cumbrous expressions, we shall usually not write charge state and spin direction explicitly, but shall use an italic k to denote a state with momentum $\mathbf{k}$ and some particular charge state and spin direction. If there is no dependence on spin and charge, a sum over states can be replaced by $4\upsilon(2\pi)^{-3}\int d^3k$, where υ is the volume of the system, and the factor 4 comes from the sum over charge states and spin directions.

Using this notation, we can write the ground state energy, given by Eq. (3.8), as

$$E_0 = (\upsilon/2\pi^3)\int \theta(k_F - k)(\hbar^2 k^2/2M)d^3k$$

$$+ \tfrac{1}{2}(\upsilon/2\pi^3)^2 \iint \theta(k_F - k)\theta(k_F - k')\langle V_{kk',kk'} - V_{kk',k'k}\rangle \, d^3k\,d^3k'. \quad (3.20)$$

We use $\theta(k_F - k)$ to denote the function which is unity for $k_F > k$, and zero for $k_F < k$. The matrix elements are averaged over charge and spin states. We have assumed that the Fermi momentum $\hbar k_F$ is the same for protons and neutrons. If we wish to evaluate the symmetry energy, the fourth term on the right of Eq. (3.18), we have to take a slightly different Fermi momentum for the protons and the neutrons. The density is

$$\rho = 2k_F^3/3\pi^2, \quad (3.21)$$

and so the average energy per particle is

$$-a_1(k_F) = 3\hbar^2 k_F^2/10M$$

$$+ (3\upsilon/16\pi^4 k_F^3) \iint \theta(k_F - k)\theta(k_F - k')\langle V_{kk',kk'} - V_{kk',k'k}\rangle \, d^3k\,d^3k'. \quad (3.22)$$

The experimental value of k_F, according to the electron scattering measurements quoted in the previous section, is 1.36×10^{13} cm^{-1}, so that the kinetic energy is about 23 Mev per particle, and the potential energy must be -39 Mev per particle to give the observed total energy.

This formula has been used for calculating the energy and density of nuclear matter by Euler (1937) and Huby (1949). It is not possible to use an ordinary attractive potential, since this would give a very large and negative contribution to Eq. (3.22) for large k_F, and there would be no equilibrium density; the dependence of energy on k_F for such a

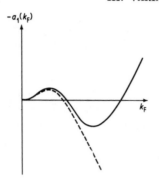

FIG. 1. Energy per particle in nuclear matter as a function of the Fermi momentum $\hbar k_F$. The broken curve would be obtained from a potential with no exchange mixture, and the solid curve from a potential with enough exchange to give saturation.

potential is shown by the dashed curve in Fig. 1. The exchange forces, which can be used to explain the saturation of nuclear forces, are attractive in some states of relative angular momentum and spin, and repulsive in others, and for such forces there is an equilibrium density for which $-a_1(k_F)$ has a minimum value. In these calculations of Euler and of Huby, which use exchange forces, the average energy is found to depend on k_F in the way shown by the solid curve of Fig. 1. The position of the minimum of the curve gives the binding energy per particle and the equilibrium density, while the curvature at the minimum gives the compressibility. In both these calculations, when the potentials used fit the low-energy data on nucleon-nucleon scattering, the calculated equilibrium density and binding energy are less than the observed values. The type of potential used in these calculations does not fit the high-energy scattering data, so we consider the question of improving on these calculations in the next chapter.

6. Alternative solutions of the Hartree-Fock equations

It is easy to interpret that part of the solid curve of Fig. 1 which lies beyond the minimum. If the particles are put under pressure, the density increases, and the curve shown could be a reasonable approximation for the variation of energy with density in this region. If k_F is below the value at which the average energy is a minimum, no such interpretation is possible, since a negative pressure cannot be imposed on a system. In fact it is clear that if the particle density is below the equilibrium density, a determinant of plane waves is no longer the determinant which gives the lowest expectation value of the Hamiltonian. A lower energy could obviously be obtained by dividing the total volume into two portions, so that all the particles were concentrated in one portion, where they would have their equilibrium density; the basis wave functions would all vanish in the second portion of the volume. The determinant would then represent something like a condensed liquid.

There is another obvious example of a case in which a determinant of plane waves does not give the best solution of the Hartree-Fock equations. Suppose that the potential between two particles is very large and positive when the particles are close together, but is negative at larger distances. This is the sort of potential which acts between two molecules, which always repel one another if they are brought too close together. The expectation value of the potential energy for a determinant of plane waves is very large and positive, because the particles overlap in such a configuration. If a determinant of wave functions which do not overlap is used, there is more kinetic energy, but the potential energy is much reduced. We can prevent the basis wave functions from overlapping by making each one vanish outside a small local region, using a different region for each wave function. This represents a system in the solid state, but it should still be possible to find a solution of the Hartree-Fock equations to describe such a system.

Interest in such possibilities has been increased by a suggestion by Overhauser (1960) that the best solution of the Hartree-Fock equations for nuclear matter might give a fluctuating density. In the paper quoted, this idea is not developed far, and has been subject to some criticism. We might expect, in view of the tight binding of alpha-particles, that the best solution for nuclear matter might describe a lattice in which two neutrons and two protons are localized near each point of the lattice. There is not much experimental evidence, however, for the existence of such clusters in medium or heavy nuclei. It has been observed by Gross (1960a) that the formation of such a lattice does not mean that the system is a solid. At the time of writing, the situation is unclear.

It is not easy to guess what the best solution of the Hartree-Fock equations is like, but we can find an additional condition that a particular solution must satisfy if it is the best solution. The condition is that no infinitesimal change of the basis wave functions may decrease the expectation value of the Hamiltonian. We refer to a solution which satisfies this condition as *stable*. The condition for stability is a condition on the eigenvalues of a certain matrix, and we now derive this condition. It is convenient first to find an expression for a general determinantal wave function in the notation of second quantization.

Using second quantization, the wave function of Eq. (3.1) can be written as

$$|\Phi\rangle = (\prod_{i=1}^{N} a_i{}^\dagger)|0\rangle, \tag{3.23}$$

where $|0\rangle$ is the vacuum, the state with no particles. A general N-particle determinant can be written as

$$|\Phi'\rangle = \{\prod_{\alpha=1}^{N}(\sum_{i=1}^{N} f_{\alpha i}a_i{}^\dagger + \sum_{m=N+1}^{\infty} f_{\alpha m}a_m{}^\dagger)\}|0\rangle. \qquad (3.24)$$

If this state is not orthogonal to $|\Phi\rangle$, we can normalize it so that

$$\langle\Phi|\Phi'\rangle = \det f_{\alpha i} = 1. \qquad (3.25)$$

We write the inverse of the $N \times N$ matrix $f_{\alpha i}$ as $F_{i\alpha}$, so that

$$\sum_{i=1}^{N} f_{\alpha i}F_{i\beta} = \delta_{\alpha\beta}, \qquad \sum_{\alpha=1}^{N} F_{i\alpha}f_{\alpha j} = \delta_{ij}, \qquad (3.25)$$

and then define

$$C_{mi} = \sum_{\alpha} F_{i\alpha}f_{\alpha m} \qquad (3.27)$$

for $m > N$. The N basis wave functions of the determinant (3.24) are

$$\sum_{i=1}^{\infty} f_{\alpha i}a_i{}^\dagger|0\rangle$$

and N linear combinations of these are

$$\sum_{\alpha=1}^{N} F_{j\alpha}\sum_{i=1}^{\infty} f_{\alpha i}a_i{}^\dagger|0\rangle = (a_j{}^\dagger + \sum_{m=N+1}^{\infty} C_{mj}a_m{}^\dagger)|0\rangle$$

$$= (1 + \sum_{m=N+1}^{\infty} C_{mj}a_m{}^\dagger a_j)a_j{}^\dagger|0\rangle. \qquad (3.28)$$

The determinant of these is identical with $|\Phi'\rangle$, and so we have

$$|\Phi'\rangle = \{\prod_{j=1}^{N}(1 + \sum_{m=N+1}^{\infty} C_{mj}a_m{}^\dagger a_j)a_j{}^\dagger\}|0\rangle$$

$$= \{\prod_{j=1}^{N}\prod_{m=N+1}^{\infty}(1 + C_{mj}a_m{}^\dagger a_j)\}|\Phi\rangle$$

$$= \{\exp(\sum_{j=1}^{N}\sum_{m=N+1}^{\infty} C_{mj}a_m{}^\dagger a_j)\}|\Phi\rangle, \qquad (3.29)$$

where we have used the anticommutation relations (2.9), which imply that $a_j{}^2$ and $a_m{}^{\dagger 2}$ are zero. This expression represents any N-particle determinant which is not orthogonal to $|\Phi\rangle$, and it enables us to find the condition for $|\Phi\rangle$ to give a local minimum of the expectation value of the Hamiltonian in a simple manner.

We have to evaluate the expectation value of the Hamiltonian (3.4) up to second order in the numbers C_{mj}. Since $|\Phi\rangle$ is a solution of the Hartree-Fock equations, there are no first order terms, and we get, by use of Eqs. (3.7) and (3.8),

$$\langle\Phi'|\Phi'\rangle = 1 + \sum_{i=1}^{N} \sum_{m=N+1}^{\infty} |C_{mi}|^2,$$

$$\langle\Phi'|H|\Phi'\rangle = E_0\langle\Phi'|\Phi'\rangle + \sum_{i=1}^{N} \sum_{m=N+1}^{\infty} (\epsilon_m - \epsilon_i)|C_{mi}|^2$$

$$+ \sum_{i=1}^{N} \sum_{j=1}^{N} \sum_{m=N+1}^{\infty} \sum_{n=N+1}^{\infty} [(V_{in,mj} - V_{in,jm})C_{nj}{}^*C_{mi}$$

$$+\tfrac{1}{2}(V_{ij,mn} - V_{ij,nm})C_{mi}C_{nj}+\tfrac{1}{2}(V_{mn,ij} - V_{mn,ji})C_{mi}{}^*C_{nj}{}^*]. \quad (3.30)$$

Here we have a quadratic form in the numbers C_{mi} which must be non-negative definite for the solution to be stable. The eigenvalues λ of the quadratic form are given by

$$(\epsilon_m - \epsilon_i)C_{mi} + \sum_{j=1}^{N} \sum_{n=N+1}^{\infty} [(V_{mj,in} - V_{mj,ni})C_{nj}$$

$$+ (V_{mn,ij} - V_{mn,ji})C_{nj}{}^*]=\lambda C_{mi},$$

$$(\epsilon_m - \epsilon_i)C_{mi}{}^* + \sum_{j=1}^{N} \sum_{n=N+1}^{\infty} [(V_{ij,mn} - V_{ij,nm})C_{nj}$$

$$+ (V_{in,mj} - V_{in,jm})C_{nj}{}^*]=\lambda C_{mi}{}^*, \quad (3.31)$$

and the condition for stability is that every λ should be positive or zero. A discussion of the physical interpretation of this equation is given in Chapter V, Sec. 10.

We can apply this equation to the case of an infinite system of particles interacting by means of a δ-function potential. We test whether a determinant of plane waves minimizes the expectation value of the Hamiltonian. For simplicity we assume that there is only one kind of particle, which has spin one half. Matrix elements of the potential conserve momentum. Because of the effect of the exclusion principle in keeping similar particles away from one another, there is interaction only between particles of opposite spin, and all the nonvanishing matrix elements are equal to a constant $V/\mathcal{V}$. The Hartree-Fock energies are all shifted the same amount by the interaction, so that Eq. (3.31) becomes

$$[\hbar^2(2\mathbf{k}\cdot\mathbf{q}-q^2)/2M - \lambda]C(\mathbf{k} + \mathbf{q}, \sigma; \mathbf{k}, \sigma)$$

$$+ (V/8\pi^3)\int[C(\mathbf{k}' + \mathbf{q}, -\sigma; \mathbf{k}', -\sigma)$$

$$+ C^*(\mathbf{k}' - \mathbf{q}, -\sigma; \mathbf{k}', -\sigma)]\,d^3k' = 0 \quad (3.32\text{a})$$

and its complex conjugate, and

$$[\hbar^2(2\mathbf{k}\cdot\mathbf{q} - q^2)/2M - \lambda]C(\mathbf{k} + \mathbf{q}, \sigma; \mathbf{k}, -\sigma)$$

$$- (V/8\pi^3)\int[C(\mathbf{k}' + \mathbf{q}, \sigma; \mathbf{k}', -\sigma)$$

$$+ C^*(\mathbf{k}' - \mathbf{q}, -\sigma; \mathbf{k}', \sigma)]\,d^3k' = 0 \quad (3.32\text{b})$$

and its complex conjugate. Here we have written $C(\mathbf{k} + \mathbf{q}, \sigma; \mathbf{k}, \sigma')$ for C_{mi} when m is the level with momentum $\mathbf{k} + \mathbf{q}$ and spin direction σ, while i is the level with momentum $\mathbf{k}$ and spin direction σ'. We can solve these two eigenvalue problems by multiplying each equation by

$$[\hbar^2(2\mathbf{k}\cdot\mathbf{q} - q^2)/2M - \lambda]^{-1}$$

and integrating over $\mathbf{k}$. From the two sets of equations we get an equation of the form

$$\begin{vmatrix} 1 \pm A & \pm A \\ \pm A & 1 \pm A \end{vmatrix} = 0, \quad (3.33)$$

where the plus sign comes from Eq. (3.32a), and the minus sign from Eq. (3.32b). The number A is given by

$$A = \frac{V}{8\pi^3\hbar^3}\int_{|\mathbf{k}+\mathbf{q}|>k_F}^{k<k_F} [\hbar^2(2\mathbf{k}\cdot\mathbf{q} - q^2)/2M - \lambda]^{-1}\,d^3k$$

$$= \frac{V}{8\pi^3\hbar^3}\int_{|\mathbf{k}-\mathbf{q}|>k_F}^{k<k_F} [\hbar^2(-2\mathbf{k}\cdot\mathbf{q} - q^2)/2M - \lambda]^{-1}\,d^3k. \quad (3.34)$$

The condition for λ to be positive is then

$$\frac{|V|}{4\pi^3\hbar^3}\int_{|\mathbf{k}+\mathbf{q}|>k_F}^{k<k_F} [\hbar(2\mathbf{k}\cdot\mathbf{q} - q^2)/2M]^{-1}\,d^3k \leq 1. \quad (3.35)$$

The left hand side of this inequality tends to its maximum value as q tends to zero, and it has the limit $Mk_F V/2\pi^2\hbar^2$, so that the condition for stability is

$$|V| \leq 2\pi^2\hbar^2/Mk_F. \quad (3.36)$$

This result has a simple interpretation. If the local densities of particles with spin up and spin down are n_+ and n_-, the energy density is

$$E(n_+, n_-) = (3\hbar^2/10M)(6\pi^2)^{2/3}(n_+^{5/3} + n_-^{5/3}) + Vn_+n_-. \quad (3.37)$$

If the integral of δ, the departure of the density from a uniform value, over all space is zero, then, up to second order in δ, we have

$$\int E(n + \delta, n \pm \delta) \approx \int E(n, n) + \left(\frac{\hbar^2(6\pi^2)^{2/3}}{3Mn^{1/3}} \mp V\right)\int \delta^2. \quad (3.38)$$

If we put $n = k_F^3/6\pi^2$, we see that (3.36) is the condition for the energy not to decrease for small departures from the uniform distribution. For V negative, the instability may be caused by fluctuations of the total density, in which the two spin populations behave in the same way, whereas for V positive, the instability may be caused by spin fluctuations, in which the two spin populations vary in opposite ways.

7. Jastrow's method

In a number of problems, we are concerned with particles that repel one another very strongly when they approach one another too closely. We call the region in which the potential is large and positive the *hard core*. The best solution of the Hartree-Fock equations must be a determinant of localized wave functions, so that the hard cores do not overlap. This is reasonable enough for systems whose density is high, so that the particles are packed close together; the wave function describes a solid. However, there are some systems which have a fluid ground state, although the potential has a hard core. The core radius must be considerably less than the average separation of the particles for this to occur. Liquid He^3 is one such system, and nuclear matter is another, since there is evidence that nucleons repel one another strongly when they are less than 0.5×10^{-13} cm apart.[†] The Hartree-Fock solution is obviously a bad approximation in such cases.

A form of trial wave function which is better than a single determinant has been suggested by Jastrow (1955). This trial wave function is

$$\Phi = f(r_{12})f(r_{13})\cdots\cdot f(r_{ij})\cdots\cdot \det \Phi_i(r_j) \quad (3.39)$$

where r_{ij} is the distance between the particles i and j. This is a determinant multiplied by a factor from each pair of particles, and this factor is a single function of the separation of the particles. The wave function is properly antisymmetric, and, by making $f(r)$ vanish for r

[†] See H. A. Bethe and P. Morrison, "Elementary Nuclear Theory," Wiley, New York, 1956, pp. 129–131, for a discussion of this.

less thán the core radius, we can prevent the strong repulsion from making an unnecessary increase in the expectation value of the potential energy without much increasing the kinetic energy.

The difficulty with this method is that an explicit expression for the expectation value of the Hamiltonian cannot be obtained. The usual method of evaluating it is to use the first few terms in what is known as the "cluster expansion" of this expectation value, which is justifiable if the core radius is small compared with the particle separation. A review of this method has been given by Aviles (1958). It has been applied to the theory of nuclear matter by Iwamoto and Yamada (1957), and has been used to calculate the binding energy of a finite nucleus by Dabrowski (1958). Since Dabrowski showed that this expansion leads to a simplified form of the Brueckner theory, we do not discuss it any further except in connection with the Brueckner theory.

8. The shell model

The theory of nuclear matter enables us to study some of the general properties of medium and heavy nuclei, but the *shell model* of the nucleus is able to account in detail for many of the observed properties of actual nuclei; this is described in the book by Mayer and Jensen (1955). We devote more attention to the theory of nuclear matter than to the shell model because of the close relation between nuclear matter and other extended systems (liquid He^3 and the electron gas), and because calculations are rather simpler. The shell model must be used as a starting-point for any detailed calculation.

In the shell model, the nucleons are supposed to move independently in a common potential well. The energy levels for a particle moving in the well are arranged in a series of shells, with a considerable separation in energy between each shell. The high binding energy of nuclei in which the protons or neutrons exactly fill a certain number of shells is one of the most striking pieces of evidence for the shell model; such nuclei are called closed shell nuclei.

This is just the sort of picture of the nucleus which the Hartree-Fock equations would give us. The difficulty is that the forces between nucleons are so strong that we have no reason to expect the Hartree-Fock equations to give a good description of the ground state of a nucleus. Nevertheless, some useful information might be obtained by doing Hartree-Fock calculations for finite nuclei, using some potential, not necessarily closely related to the real nucleon-nucleon potential, chosen to give the right sort of results for nuclear matter. No systematic calculations of this sort have been done.

Without actually making a calculation, we can deduce some general properties which the self-consistent potential should have. In the central region of the nucleus, the potential should resemble the potential for nuclear matter, the second term on the right of Eq. (3.19). This term does not depend on the position, but does depend on the momentum of the particle. In the surface region also, the potential should presumably be nonlocal, but no other properties are obvious in this region. A closed shell nucleus should be spherically symmetric, but additional particles outside the closed shell should destroy the spherical symmetry, and, if there are many particles outside closed shells, a spheroidal shape may be more stable. There is conclusive evidence that nuclei with many particles outside closed shells are strongly distorted from a spherical shape; this evidence has been reviewed by Temmer (1958).

For spherical nuclei, angular momentum conservation plays the same role as linear momentum conservation does in the theory of nuclear matter; we use eigenstates of angular momentum instead of eigenstates of momentum for our single-particle levels. If two particles interact, angular momentum is conserved, so that matrix elements of the Hamiltonian between configurations with different angular momenta vanish. The complications of this representation are that the law of addition of angular momenta is more complicated than the law of addition of linear momenta in quantum mechanics, and that only two quantities (total angular momentum and the projection of angular momentum in one direction) instead of three (the components of linear momentum in three directions) are conserved. For spheroidal nuclei, only the projection of the angular momentum is conserved.

The *optical model* is closely related to the shell model. The elastic scattering of nucleons from the nucleus can be calculated by replacing the nucleus by a potential well with a small imaginary (absorptive) part. This model was suggested by Fernbach and co-workers (1949) and developed by Feshbach and associates (1954). This potential well is similar to the shell model potential, and it is clear that the success of the shell model and the success of the optical model are closely connected. It is found necessary to assume a momentum dependence of the potential, in agreement with our remarks on the shell model potential; the dependence of the potential on momentum is analyzed in an article by Glassgold (1959).

IV. Perturbation Theory

1. General discussion

In principle, perturbation methods enable us to start with a soluble problem and to proceed systematically to the solution of a physical problem. In many-body problems, it is often convenient to start with the problem of noninteracting particles, and to regard the interactions as a perturbation. Although it is quite easy to write down a series expansion for the effect of the perturbation, it is usually very difficult to evaluate more than two or three of the terms in the expansion, or to determine whether or not the series is convergent. The usefulness of an expansion depends not so much on whether it is convergent, but on whether the leading terms give a good approximation.

An example of an expansion in which the behaviour of the first few terms is misleading has been given by Bethe (1956). The Brillouin-Wigner perturbation expansion is usually regarded as an improvement on the Rayleigh-Schrödinger perturbation expansion for a one-body problem, but it is quite unsuitable for a many-body problem. If the unperturbed Hamiltonian is H_0, with eigenstate $|\Phi_0\rangle$ and eigenvalue W_0, the true Hamiltonian $H = H_0 + H_1$ has an eigenstate $|\Psi_0\rangle$ with eigenvalue E_0, where

$$|\Psi_0\rangle = |\Phi_0\rangle + \frac{P}{E_0 - H_0} H_1 |\Psi_0\rangle, \qquad (4.1)$$

and

$$E_0 = W_0 + \langle \Phi_0 | H_1 | \Psi_0 \rangle. \qquad (4.2)$$

The operator P in Eq. (4.1) is the projection operator which projects off the state $|\Phi_0\rangle$, given by

$$P = 1 - |\Phi_0\rangle\langle\Phi_0|. \qquad (4.3)$$

The state $|\Phi_0\rangle$ is normalized to unity, but $|\Psi_0\rangle$ is normalized so that its scalar product with $|\Phi_0\rangle$ is unity. It can easily be seen that the equation

$$(H_0 - W_0) |\Phi_0\rangle = 0 \qquad (4.4)$$

can be combined with Eqs. (4.1) and (4.2) to give

$$(H - E_0)|\Psi_0\rangle = (H_0 + H_1 - E_0)|\Psi_0\rangle = 0. \qquad (4.5)$$

The expansion of Eq. (4.2) which is obtained by iterating Eq. (4.1) is

$$E_0 = W_0 + \langle\Phi_0|H_1|\Phi_0\rangle + \langle\Phi_0|H_1 \frac{P}{E_0 - H_0} H_1|\Phi_0\rangle + \cdots, \qquad (4.6)$$

and this is the Brillouin-Wigner expansion.

We analyze the behaviour of the terms of this expansion as the total number of particles N increases, while the density remains constant. If H_0 is the Hamiltonian for noninteracting particles and H_1 is the two-body interaction between the particles, then $|\Phi_0\rangle$ is a determinant of plane waves. The interaction H_1 can either change the state of two particles or of none; the diagonal matrix elements of H_1 are proportional to N, but the nondiagonal elements are proportional to N^{-1}. The first two terms on the right of Eq. (4.6) are proportional to N. Since the intermediate configurations of the third term differ from the initial configuration only by the levels of two particles, the value of H_0 differs from W_0 by an amount independent of N. However, E_0 differs from W_0 by an amount proportional to N, so that $(E_0 - H_0)$ is proportional to N in this term. The number of possible intermediate configurations is proportional to N^3, since any two of the particles may be excited to any pair of levels with the same total momentum. We have found three factors of N^{-1} and one of N^3, so the third term on the right of Eq. (4.6) is independent of N. In general, any further term of the expansion will be independent of N. This does not mean that, in the limit of large N, the first two terms of the expansion are sufficient, but simply that the convergence is very slow.

An expansion which does seem to be suitable for many-body problems is the Rayleigh-Schrödinger expansion. This is a direct expansion of the energy as a power series in the strength of the interaction, so that each term has the right dependence on N. The Schrödinger equation can be written as

$$|\Psi_0\rangle = |\Phi_0\rangle + \frac{P}{W_0 - H_0}(H_1 - E_0 + W_0)|\Psi_0\rangle,$$
$$E_0 - W_0 = \langle\Phi_0|H_1|\Psi_0\rangle. \qquad (4.7)$$

If E_0 and $|\Psi_0\rangle$ are *both* expanded at the same time, and the terms are grouped according to the number of powers of H_1 they contain, the Rayleigh-Schrödinger expansion is obtained. The first few terms are

$$E_0 = W_0 + \langle\Phi_0|H_1|\Phi_0\rangle + \langle\Phi_0|H_1 \frac{P}{W_0 - H_0} H_1|\Phi_0\rangle + \cdots. \qquad (4.8)$$

The third term is proportional to N, unlike the third term of Eq. (4.6), because $(E_0 - H_0)$ has been replaced by $(W_0 - H_0)$. The higher terms of this expansion are quite complicated when written out like this, so we develop a more convenient notation for them in the next three sections.

We shall always be concerned with the calculation of the expectation value of an operator, not with the calculation of the wave function. The reason is that the wave function of a many-body system is so complicated that any approximation to it will be almost orthogonal to it. Our criterion for a good wave function must therefore be that it should give good approximations for the expectation values of physical observables, not that it should be nearly parallel to the true wave function. Either criterion is possible in one-particle perturbation theory. The reason for this difference is that if a particle has probability a of being excited from an approximate wave function, the probability of all the particles being unexcited is $(1 - a)^N$; this goes like $\exp(-aN)$ for large N, and this is exponentially small even if a is very small. The error in the expectation value of a one-particle operator should simply be proportional to a.

2. The Goldstone-Hugenholtz graphical method

The representation of terms in the perturbation series by *graphs* was found by Feynman (1949) to be very useful in field theory. The same technique was used by Goldstone (1957) and Hugenholtz (1957) in their analyses of perturbation theory for many-fermion systems. The methods used by these two authors are closely related, since Goldstone uses an expansion of the *development operator*

$$U(t) = \exp(-iHt), \qquad (4.9)$$

while Hugenholtz expands the *resolvent*

$$R(z) = (H - z)^{-1}. \qquad (4.10)$$

These operators are related by

$$R(z) = -i \int_{-\infty}^{0} U(t) \exp(izt) dt, \quad \text{for} \quad \text{Im } z < 0,$$

$$R(z) = i \int_{0}^{\infty} U(t) \exp(izt) dt, \quad \text{for} \quad \text{Im } z > 0. \qquad (4.11)$$

The development operator describes the way in which a system develops in time, if t is the time divided by $\hbar$. The expansion of $U(t)$ is easier to manipulate, since we generally have to deal with products of functions rather than with the convolutions of functions which arise in the expansion of $R(z)$. The resolvent has a more direct physical interpretation, since the poles of its matrix elements give the eigenvalues of the Hamiltonian.

We split up the Hamiltonian into

$$H = H_0 + H_1, \tag{4.12}$$

and use of the expansion of $U(t)$ given by Dyson (1949a),

$$\exp{(iH_0t)} U(t) = 1 - i \int_0^t \exp{(iH_0t_1)} H_1 \exp{(-iH_0t_1)} \, dt_1$$

$$+ (-i)^2 \int_0^t dt_2 \int_0^{t_2} dt_1 \exp{(iH_0t_2)} H_1 \exp{(-iH_0t_2)}$$

$$\times \exp{(iH_0t_1)} H_1 \exp{(-iH_0t_1)} + \cdots$$

$$= \sum_{n=0}^{\infty} \frac{(-i)^n}{n!} \int_0^t \cdots \int_0^t T[H_1(t_n) \cdots H_1(t_2) H_1(t_1)] dt_1 \cdots dt_n. \tag{4.13}$$

Here the time-dependent operators $H_1(t)$ are defined by

$$H_1(t) = \exp(iH_0t) H_1 \exp(-iH_0t), \tag{4.14}$$

and, in general,

$$Q(t) = \exp(iH_0t) Q \exp(-iH_0t); \tag{4.15}$$

this is the so-called interaction picture. The letter T followed by a square bracket denotes a product of the operators inside the bracket rearranged so that the arguments decrease from left to right; this is called a time-ordered product. Equation (4.13) gives a correct expansion for $U(t)$, since it satisfies

$$(d/dt) U(t) = -iH U(t),$$

$$U(0) = 1. \tag{4.16}$$

We apply this method to an extended system, taking the unperturbed ground state $|\Phi_0\rangle$ to be a determinant of plane waves. There is no fundamental difficulty about applying it to finite systems, but the theory does have a slightly simpler form for infinite systems. The state $|\Phi_0\rangle$ plays the same part in this theory as the (unperturbed) vacuum does in field theory, and we describe an arbitrary configuration of the N-particle system by saying how it differs from $|\Phi_0\rangle$.

We have to distinguish between levels which are occupied in $|\Phi_0\rangle$ and those which are unoccupied. We use the letter l to denote a state with momentum less than the Fermi momentum $\hbar k_F$, and the letter m to denote a state with momentum greater than the Fermi momentum. We rewrite the creation and annihilation operators $a_k{}^\dagger$ and a_k as

$$a_l = \xi_l{}^\dagger, \qquad a_l{}^\dagger = \xi_l, \quad \text{for} \quad l < k_F,$$

$$a_m = \eta_m, \qquad a_m{}^\dagger = \eta_m{}^\dagger, \quad \text{for} \quad m > k_F, \qquad (4.17)$$

and call $\xi_l{}^\dagger$ the creation operator for a *hole* and $\eta_m{}^\dagger$ the creation operator for a *particle*. The anticommutation relations still have the same form as in Eq. (2.9). The determinant $|\Phi_0\rangle$ is like the vacuum of field theory, since we have

$$\xi_l |\Phi_0\rangle = \eta_m |\Phi_0\rangle = 0, \qquad (4.18)$$

so that it is the state with no "particles" and no holes in it. We call $\eta_m{}^\dagger |\Phi_0\rangle$ a one-particle configuration, and we call $\xi_l{}^\dagger |\Phi_0\rangle$ a one-hole configuration. Configurations of N physical particles have the same number of "particles" as holes.

We take the unperturbed Hamiltonian and the perturbation to be

$$H_0 = \sum_k T_k a_k{}^\dagger a_k = \sum_{l<k_F} T_l \xi_l \xi_l{}^\dagger + \sum_{m>k_F} T_m \eta_m{}^\dagger \eta_m,$$

$$H_1 = \tfrac{1}{2} \sum V_{k_1 k_2, k_3 k_4} a_{k_2}{}^\dagger a_{k_1}{}^\dagger a_{k_3} a_{k_4}, \qquad (4.19)$$

and we can represent the terms in the perturbation series (4.13) for $\langle \Phi | U(t) | \Phi_0 \rangle$ by graphs in the following way. We take a particular term in the series (4.13), with particular configurations in the intermediate states, and with particular values of the integration variables. We use a vertical time-scale from 0 to t running up the diagram, and we draw a horizontal dotted line at the time coordinate t' to denote $H_1(t')$. The intermediate state at a particular time is represented by drawing solid directed lines which go up to represent "particles" in the intermediate state and which go down to represent holes. We label the lines to show which holes or particles they represent. These *fermion lines* can only end at dotted lines, interactions, as the configuration cannot change elsewhere. Examples of the diagrams which contribute to the second order term in the expansion of $\langle \Phi_0 | U(t) | \Phi_0 \rangle$ are shown in Fig. 2. These represent

$$\langle \Phi_0 | H_1(t_2) | \Phi' \rangle \langle \Phi' | H_1(t_1) | \Phi_0 \rangle,$$

where $|\Phi'\rangle$ is the configuration $\eta_l{}^\dagger \eta_m{}^\dagger \eta_{l'}{}^\dagger \eta_{m'}{}^\dagger |\Phi_0\rangle$. Figure 2(a) gives a contribution

$$(-i)^2 |V_{ll',mm'}|^2 \exp[i(T_m + T_{m'} - T_l - T_{l'})(t_1 - t_2)]$$

while Fig. 2(b) gives a contribution

$$(-i)^2 V_{ll'mm'} \exp[i(T_m + T_{m'} - T_l - T_{l'})(t_1 - t_2)] V_{m'm,ll'}$$

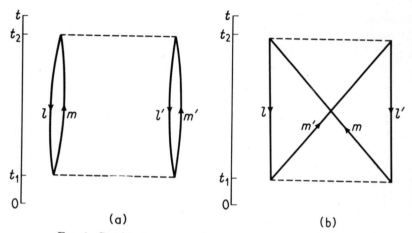

FIG. 2. Graphical representation of second order processes.

to $\langle \Phi_0 | U(t) | \Phi_0 \rangle$. To get the complete contribution of such graphs, we must still sum over all distinct intermediate configurations, and integrate over all times such that $t > t_2 > t_1 > 0$.

3. Wick's thoerem

The analysis of the series (4.13) in terms of graphs is made much easier by using a theorem due to Wick (1950). This theorem gives the relation between a time-ordered product of operators, such as occurs in Eq. (4.13), and a *normal product*, in which all the creation operators stand to the left of the annihilation operators.

We define a normal product in terms of the creation operators $\xi^\dagger$ and $\eta^\dagger$, and the annihilation operators ξ and η, which were defined by Eq. (4.17). The normal product of a number of such operators is defined as the product of the operators rearranged so that creation operators stand to the left of annihilation operators, with a minus sign if the rearrangement involves an odd number of permutations of the operators. For example, we have

$$N[\xi_l \xi_{l'}{}^\dagger \eta_m{}^\dagger \eta_{m'}] = -\xi_{l'}{}^\dagger \eta_m{}^\dagger \eta_{m'} \xi_l. \qquad (4.20)$$

The order of the creation operators or of the annihilation operators among themselves does not matter, since they anticommute. The distributive law

$$N[(A + B)C] = N[AC] + N[BC] \qquad (4.21)$$

allows us to calculate a normal product of operators which are not just simple annihilation or creation operators, but which may be sums of annihilation and creation operators. From our definition, the expectation value for $|\Phi_0\rangle$ of the normal product of any number of creation and annihilation operators is zero; only the normal product of a number is nonzero. This follows from Eq. (4.18), since the annihilation operators on the right of the product give zero when $|\Phi_0\rangle$ stands to their right, and the creation operators on the left of the product give zero when $\langle\Phi_0|$ stands to their left.

In the perturbation series (4.13) for $\exp(iH_0t)U(t)$ we have time-ordered products, in which operators with a particular time argument stand to the left of those with earlier time arguments. The interaction H_1 is, according to Eq. (4.19), a product of four creation or annihilation operators, which all, of course, have the same argument, so we define a time-ordered product so that, if some of the operators have the same argument, the operators $a^\dagger$ (in our notation ξ_l and $\eta_m{}^\dagger$) stand to the left of the operators a (in our notation, $\xi_l{}^\dagger$ and η_m). There is again a minus sign for an odd permutation of the fermion operators, and a time-ordered product also obeys the distributive law

$$T[(A + B)C] = T[AC] + T[BC]. \qquad (4.22)$$

An example of a time-ordered product is

$$T[\xi_l(t_1)\eta_m(t_2)\eta_{m'}{}^\dagger(t_2)\xi_{l'}{}^\dagger(t_1)] = -\xi_l(t_1)\xi_{l'}{}^\dagger(t_1)\eta_{m'}{}^\dagger(t_2)\eta_m(t_2) \quad (4.23)$$

for $t_1 > t_2$.

We call the difference between the time-ordered product and the normal product of two operators the *contraction* of the operators, and denote it by putting the same number of heavy dots on each operator. The contraction is only defined for two operators U and V each of which is a simple creation or annihilation operator; it is not defined if U or V is a product of several creation or annihilation operators. The contraction is defined by

$$U^\bullet V^\bullet = T[UV] - N[UV], \qquad (4.24)$$

and it is clearly a number, since it is either equal to zero, or to plus or minus the anticommutator of the operators U and V. Wick's theorem states

$$T[UV\cdots XYZ] = N[UV\cdots XYZ] + N[U^\bullet V^\bullet \cdots XYZ]$$
$$+ N[U^\bullet VW^\bullet \cdots XYZ]$$
$$+ \cdots + N[U^\bullet V^{\bullet\bullet}W^{\bullet\bullet\bullet} \cdots X^\bullet Y^{\bullet\bullet}Z^{\bullet\bullet\bullet}]. \quad (4.25)$$

The time-ordered product is equal to the normal product of the operators, plus the sum of the normal products of the operators with one pair contracted, the pair being chosen in all possible ways, plus the sum of the normal products with two contractions, and so on. A contraction inside a normal product is just a number, but a sign change must be made if an odd number of permutations is needed to remove the contracted pair from the normal product:

$$N[U^\bullet V^\bullet W^{\bullet\bullet} X^{\bullet\bullet}] = (U^\bullet V^\bullet)(W^{\bullet\bullet} X^{\bullet\bullet}),$$
$$N[U^\bullet V^{\bullet\bullet} W^\bullet X^{\bullet\bullet}] = -(U^\bullet W^\bullet)(V^{\bullet\bullet} X^{\bullet\bullet}). \qquad (4.26)$$

The proof of this theorem is by induction. It is obvious if there are only two operators, since Eqs. (4.24) and (4.25) are equivalent in that case. If we assume that the theorem is always true for a product of n operators, we can prove it for a product of $n + 1$ operators. Suppose that the operator with the earliest time coordinate is A, so that

$$T[UV \cdots XYZA] = T[UV \cdots XYZ]A. \qquad (4.27)$$

If A is an annihilation operator, its contraction with all the other operators is zero. If we multiply Eq. (4.25) on the right by A, we can include A inside the normal products, since it is standing to the right as it should. Since all contractions involving A give zero, the theorem for $n + 1$ operators is satisfied if A is an annihilation operator. If A is a creation operator, it can be commuted through to the left of all the products on the right of Eq. (4.25) and then put inside the normal product signs. The anticommutator of A with any operator is just the contraction, and so the theorem again holds. If A is the sum of a creation and an annihilation operator, the distributive law, which holds for time-ordered products, normal products, and contractions, ensures that the theorem holds for any product of $n + 1$ operators. Since the theorem holds for $n = 2$, it must hold for all higher n.

The contraction of two operators which anticommute is clearly zero. The only pairs of operators which have a nonzero contraction are

$$a_{l'}(t_2)^\bullet a_l{}^\dagger(t_1)^\bullet = \xi_{l'}{}^\dagger(t_2)^\bullet \xi_l(t_1)^\bullet = 0, \quad \text{for} \quad t_2 > t_1,$$
$$a_{l'}(t_2)^\bullet a_l{}^\dagger(t_1)^\bullet = -\xi_l(t_1)\xi_{l'}{}^\dagger(t_2) - \xi_{l'}{}^\dagger(t_2)\xi_l(t_1)$$
$$= -\delta_{ll'} \exp[iT_l(t_1 - t_2)], \quad \text{for} \quad t_2 \leq t_1, \quad (4.28)$$

and

$$a_{m'}(t_2)^\bullet a_m{}^\dagger(t_1)^\bullet = \delta_{mm'} \exp[iT_m(t_1 - t_2)], \quad \text{for} \quad t_2 > t_1,$$
$$a_{m'}(t_2)^\bullet a_m{}^\dagger(t_1)^\bullet = 0, \quad \text{for} \quad t_2 \leq t_1. \quad (4.29)$$

These contractions are also called *unperturbed propagators*.

Wick's theorem makes it easy to calculate expectation values of operators in the configuration $|\Phi_0\rangle$. The expectation value of a normal product of operators is zero, and the only terms on the right of Eq. (4.25) which survive are those in which all the operators are contracted.

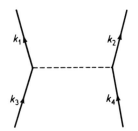

FIG. 3. Graphical representation of a matrix element of the interaction.

To evaluate the time-ordered products on the right of Eq. (4.13), we have to use Eq. (4.19) to express H_1 in terms of creation and annihilation operators, and then contract the product in all possible ways.

The process of contracting the product can be represented graphically. We draw the figure shown in Fig. 3 to represent

$$\tfrac{1}{2} V_{k_1 k_2, k_3 k_4} a_{k_2}{}^\dagger a_{k_1}{}^\dagger a_{k_3} a_{k_4},$$

and call it a *vertex*. The lines pointing into the vertex represent the levels in which particles are annihilated or holes are created by the interaction, and the lines pointing away from the vertex represent the levels in which particles are created or holes are annihilated by the interaction. We represent the product $H_1(t_n) \cdots H_1(t_2) H_1(t_1)$ by putting such a vertex at each of the levels $t_1, t_2, \cdots, t_n$; we shall have to sum over all possible incoming and outgoing momenta for each vertex. We denote a contraction by connecting two of the solid lines in this graph. The arrow must go in the same direction at each end of this connected line, since creation operators can only be contracted with annihilation operators to give a nonzero result. When all the operators have been contracted with one another, the solid lines form a system of closed loops. From the form of the contractions (4.28) and (4.29) it can be seen that a solid line joining two vertices must represent the same state at each end. Also, if a line joins a point to itself, it must be a hole line, since the contraction of two particle operators vanishes if the times are equal.

The perturbation series for $\langle \Phi_0 | \exp (i H_0 t) U(t) | \Phi_0 \rangle$ is given in this way as a sum over all graphs. The contribution of a particular graph is a product of $-\tfrac{1}{2} i$ times the matrix element of the interaction from each vertex, a contracted product from each fermion (solid) line, and a factor -1 from each closed loop of fermion lines. The factors $-i$ are the ones which occur in Eq. (4.13), and the factors -1 arise when the contractions are removed from a normal product in Eq. (4.25); a factor -1 occurs if an odd permutation of operators must be made to remove the contractions.

The graphs we obtain in this way are the same as the graphs we obtained in Sec. 2 of this chapter. The only apparent difference is that there we could not have two lines at the same time representing the same state, since this would represent a configuration with a doubly occupied level. There is no restriction of this sort in our new method; however, all these graphs which violate the exclusion principle add up to give zero.

4. Linked graphs

A graph which contributes to $\langle \Phi_0 | \exp(iH_0 t) U(t) | \Phi_0 \rangle$ may separate into two or more parts with no line connecting them, and an example is shown in Fig. 4 (a). This graph separates into two parts, each of which is like the graph of Fig. 2 (a). A graph which cannot be separated in this way is called a *linked* graph. If we call the contribution of all linked graphs to our expansion $\mathcal{L}(t)$, we can express the complete expansion in terms of $\mathcal{L}(t)$. The reason for this is that, in an unlinked graph, each linked part contributes an independent factor (this would not be true if we had to take account of the exclusion principle in intermediate states). The sum over all graphs which have n linked parts gives $[\mathcal{L}(t)]^n/n!$, since the graphs which contribute to $[\mathcal{L}(t)]^n$ are not all distinct, but each distinct graph occurs $n!$ times in the expansion of $[\mathcal{L}(t)]^n$. For example, although the two graphs shown in Figs. 4 (a) and (b) are identical, both occur in the expansion of $[\mathcal{L}(t)]^2$. Therefore the sum over all graphs gives $\exp[\mathcal{L}(t)]$, and we have

$$\mathcal{L}(t) = \log[\langle \Phi_0 | \exp(iH_0 t) U(t) | \Phi_0 \rangle]. \qquad (4.30)$$

This is the basic equation of the *linked graph expansion*. It is particularly useful for extended systems, since it was shown by Hugenholtz (1957) that every type of linked graph gives a contribution proportional to the extent of the system, and there are no terms with the

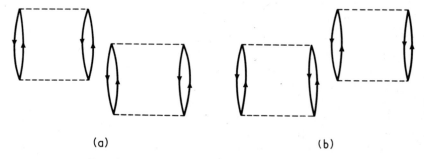

(a)   (b)

FIG. 4. Two graphs with two unlinked parts each.

wrong dependence on the volume. The expansion is still valid for finite systems. It has been remarked by Van Hove (1960), however, that the convergence of the linked graph expansion may be much worse than the convergence of the original series, since the logarithm introduces an extra singularity when its argument is zero.

We are not restricted to real values of t in this theory. If t becomes complex, we have to change the integrations in Eq. (4.13) so that all the variables run from zero to t along identical paths in the complex plane. Time-ordered products are defined as before, except that one value of the time must be called earlier than another if it comes sooner on the path from zero to t. Since the propagators (4.28) and (4.29) are analytic functions of time, the contribution of a particular graph to $\mathfrak{L}(t)$ does not depend on the path of integration chosen.

If we denote the eigenstates of H by $|\Psi_n\rangle$ and the eigenvalues by E_n, we can expand Eq. (4.30) by using this complete set of states. Making use of Eqs. (4.9) and (4.4), we get

$$\mathfrak{L}(t) = iW_0 t + \log\left[\sum_n |\langle\Phi_0|\Psi_n\rangle|^2 \exp(-iE_n t)\right]. \qquad (4.31)$$

If we take t to have a sufficiently large negative imaginary part, the contribution of the ground state to the argument of the logarithm must dominate. Therefore we get the equation for the ground state energy

$$E_0 = W_0 + i \lim_{\text{Im } t \to -\infty} \frac{d\mathfrak{L}(t)}{dt}. \qquad (4.32)$$

We can also find the magnitude of the scalar product of true wave function with the unperturbed wave function, since, from Eq. (4.31), we have

$$\log|\langle\Phi_0|\Psi_0\rangle|^2 = \lim_{\text{Im } t \to -\infty} \left[\mathfrak{L}(t) - t\frac{d\mathfrak{L}(t)}{dt}\right]. \qquad (4.33)$$

We have assumed that the ground state is not orthogonal to $|\Phi_0\rangle$. If we choose an unperturbed wave function that is orthogonal to the ground state, our perturbation procedure should give the energy of the lowest state that is not orthogonal to $|\Phi_0\rangle$.

The derivative of $\mathfrak{L}(t)$ which is required in Eq. (4.32) can be taken by fixing the last vertex at time t, since it is only those graphs with a vertex between t and $t + \delta t$ which contribute to $\mathfrak{L}(t + \delta t) - \mathfrak{L}(t)$. Since the propagators depend only on time differences, it does not matter whether we take all graphs whose last vertex is at t, or all graphs whose first vertex is at time zero, so we shall take the latter class. The vertices occur at $0, t_2, t_3, \cdots, t_n$, and we have to integrate over all the

t_2, t_3, etc. This integration is simple if we keep the order of the vertices fixed, so that we have $0 < t_2 < t_3 < \cdots < t_n < t$, since, with this restriction, the propagators (4.28) and (4.29) have an exponential form. Since we want the limit $\operatorname{Im} t \to -\infty$, we can change to the variables t_2, $t_3 - t_2$, $t_4 - t_3$, etc., and let them range from zero to infinity along a line in the lower half of the complex plane. The variables occur only in the form $\exp\left[-i(t_r - t_{r-1})D_r\right]$, where D_r is equal to the sum of the kinetic energies of the particle lines which cross a horizontal section of the graph between t_r and t_{r-1}, minus the sum of the kinetic energies of the hole lines crossing the section. The value of D_2 for Fig. 2(a) is $(T_m + T_{m'} - T_l - T_{l'})$. The integration simply gives a factor $-i/D_r$. We refer to $-D_r$ as the *energy denominator* for the region between the vertices $r - 1$ and r.

5. Rules for calculating with graphs

The argument we have used to derive the graphical formulation of perturbation theory is quite long, but the results can be expressed as a set of simple rules. We give here the rules for calculating the ground state energy of an extended system, for which the unperturbed wave function is a determinant of those plane waves with wave number less than k_F, and for which the Hamiltonian is given by Eq. (4.19). We say later how these rules must be modified in order to calculate some other quantity.

To calculate the nth order contribution to the energy, draw n horizontal broken lines at different levels. We call the two ends of each broken line *points*. We must then join up the $2n$ points with directed lines in such a way that one directed line goes into each point, and one comes out. We label each of these $2n$ directed lines with the momentum and spin of a particle state (momentum greater than $\hbar k_F$) if the line goes upwards, and with the momentum and spin of a hole state (momentum less than $\hbar k_F$) if the line goes downwards, or if it joins a point to itself or the other point at the same level. The joining of the points to one another and the labelling must be done in all possible ways. We

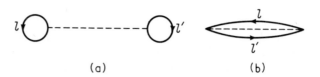

(a)   (b)

FIG. 5. Graphs that occur in the first order term for the ground state energy.

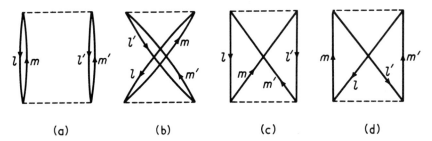

(a)   (b)   (c)   (d)

FIG. 6. Graphs that occur in the second order term for the ground state energy.

only allow linked graphs, which are those graphs which do not have two or more parts not linked to one another by any lines. The possible linked graphs for $n = 1$ and $n = 2$ are shown in Figs. 5 and 6.

The contribution of a particular linked graph is the product of the following factors:

1.) Each vertex gives a factor $\frac{1}{2}V_{k_1k_2,k_3k_4}$, where k_1 and k_2 are the lines leaving the vertex on the left and right respectively, and k_3 and k_4 are the lines entering the vertex on the left and right. In Fig. 6(a), the top vertex gives a factor $\frac{1}{2}V_{ll',mm'}$, and the bottom vertex a factor $\frac{1}{2}V_{mm',ll'}$.

2.) From each of the $n - 1$ intervals between successive vertices we get a factor equal to the reciprocal of the sum of the kinetic energies of the hole lines which cross any horizontal section between the two vertices, minus the sum of the kinetic energies of the particle lines which cross the horizontal section. For all the graphs of Fig. 6, this factor is $(T_l + T_{l'} - T_m - T_{m'})^{-1}$.

3.) There is a factor -1 for each closed loop of fermion lines, and a factor -1 for each hole line in the graph; the latter factor comes from the minus sign on the right of Eq. (4.28). These factors give $+1$ for Figs. 6(a) and 6(b), and -1 for Figs. 6(c) and 6(d).

These rules show that the contributions of Figs. 6(a) and 6(b) are the same, and of Figs. 6(c) and 6(d) are the same. The total second-order contribution to the energy is

$$W_2 = \frac{1}{2} \sum_{l<k_F} \sum_{l'<k_F} \sum_{m>k_F} \sum_{m'>k_F} (T_l + T_{l'} - T_m - T_{m'})^{-1}$$

$$\times (|V_{ll',mm'}|^2 - V_{ll',mm'}V_{mm',l'l}). \quad (4.36)$$

This result, of course, could have been obtained quite simply from Eq. (4.8).

We can use similar methods to calculate other properties of the ground state. Equation (4.33) leads to a prescription for calculating

$|\langle\Phi_0|\Psi_0\rangle|^2$; every term in the series for its logarithm is proportional to the volume of the system, so that this scalar product is exponentially small in a large system. To calculate

$$\langle\Phi_0|\, U(t)\xi_l{}^\dagger\eta_m{}^\dagger\xi_{l'}{}^\dagger\eta_{m'}{}^\dagger\,|\,\Phi_0\rangle\,\exp(iW_0t)$$

we could use Wick's theorem by drawing lines to represent l, l', m, m' at $t = 0$, and call these external lines. We would expand $U(t)$ by means of Eq. (4.13), and draw vertices to represent the interaction, joining them up with one another and with the external lines to represent contractions. The graphs would either be linked to the external lines,

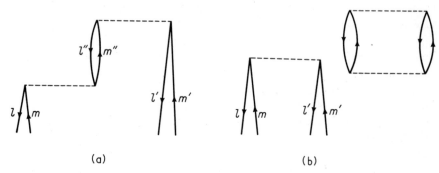

(a)   (b)

Fig. 7. A linked and an unlinked graph with two external lines.

like the graph shown in Fig. 7(a), or they would have unlinked parts, like Fig. 7(b). The sum of all graphs with certain external lines is a product of the sum of linked graphs and the sum of all graphs with no external lines. The sum of all graphs with no external lines is just $\langle\Phi_0|U(t)|\Phi_0\rangle\,\exp\,(iW_0t)$, so that, as the imaginary part of t tends to minus infinity, the sum of linked graphs gives

$$\lim_{\mathrm{Im}\,t\to-\infty}\ \langle\Phi_0|\,U(t)\xi_l{}^\dagger\eta_m{}^\dagger\xi_{l'}{}^\dagger\eta_{m'}{}^\dagger\,|\,\Phi_0\rangle/\langle\Phi_0|\,U(t)\,|\,\Phi_0\rangle$$

$$=\ \lim_{\mathrm{Im}\,t\to-\infty}\ \frac{\sum_n\langle\Phi_0|\Psi_n\rangle\exp(-iE_nt)\,\langle\Psi_n|\,\xi_l{}^\dagger\eta_m{}^\dagger\xi_{l'}{}^\dagger\eta_{m'}{}^\dagger\,|\,\Phi_0\rangle}{\sum_n|\langle\Phi_0|\Psi_n\rangle|^2\exp(-iE_nt)}$$

$$=\langle\Psi_0|\,\xi_l{}^\dagger\eta_m{}^\dagger\xi_{l'}{}^\dagger\eta_{m'}{}^\dagger\,|\,\Phi_0\rangle/\langle\Psi_0|\,\Phi_0\rangle. \qquad (4.37)$$

The amplitude relative to $\langle\Phi_0|\Psi_0\rangle$ of any component of the ground state wave function is therefore calculated by drawing all linked graphs that have the appropriate external lines which leave the graph below all the vertices. In addition to the usual factors, there will be a factor equal to the reciprocal of the sum of the kinetic energies of the external hole lines, less the sum of the kinetic energies of the external particle lines. The contribution of Fig. 7(a) to this relative amplitude is

$$\tfrac{1}{4} V_{l''l',m''m'} V_{lm'',ml''} (T_{l'} + T_{l''} - T_{m'} - T_{m''})^{-1}$$
$$\times (T_l + T_{l'} - T_m - T_{m'})^{-1}.$$

Three similar diagrams remove the factor 1/4.

The expectation value of an operator Q can be calculated in a similar way. Suppose that Q is a one-particle operator, which we can take to be

$$Q = \sum_k Q_k a_k{}^\dagger a_k, \tag{4.38}$$

since the nondiagonal elements have zero expectation value. We can calculate the value of $\langle \Phi_0 | U(t_1) Q U(t_2) | \Phi_0 \rangle \, \exp[iW_0(t_1 + t_2)]$ by using Wick's theorem. We can represent Q as a heavy dot with one line entering it and one line leaving, and put this heavy dot at the origin of the graph. The expansion of $U(t_1)$ is represented by vertices between 0 and t_1, and the expansion of $U(t_2)$ by vertices between $-t_2$ and 0. The whole graph will consist of one part which is linked to the heavy dot, and, possibly, of other parts which are unlinked. The sum of all unlinked parts gives

$$\langle \Phi_0 | U(t_1 + t_2) | \Phi_0 \rangle \, \exp[iW_0(t_1 + t_2)].$$

We can divide the sum of all graphs by this quantity to get the sum of all linked graphs. In the usual way, when we let the imaginary parts of t_1 and t_2 tend to minus infinity, we find that the sum of all linked graphs gives us $\langle \Psi_0 | Q | \Psi_0 \rangle$. We can integrate over the time coordinates, and we get the usual factors. The heavy dot counts as a vertex which contributes a factor Q_k. Some examples of such graphs are shown in Fig. 8.

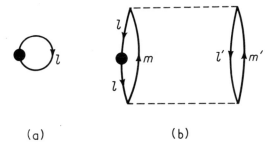

(a)   (b)

FIG. 8. Graphs that contribute to the expectation value of a one-particle operator.

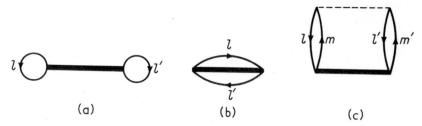

Fɪɢ. 9. Graphs that contribute to the expectation value of a two-particle operator.

Figure 8(a) gives the zero order expectation value of Q, and Fig. 8(b) contributes

$$-\tfrac{1}{4}Q_l \left| V_{ll'mm'} \right|^2 (T_l + T_{l'} - T_m - T_{m'})^{-2}.$$

If Q is a two-particle operator, it can be represented in a graph by a heavy horizontal line with fermion lines entering and leaving at each end. Its expectation value can be calculated by adding up all linked graphs which contain this element just once. Some examples are shown in Fig. 9.

6. Hartree-Fock energies

The relation of the Hartree-Fock theory to this graphical perturbation theory was shown by Goldstone (1957). Consider the series of graphs shown in Fig. 10, in which one of the lines, m, of a particular second order graph goes through one or more vertices at which another

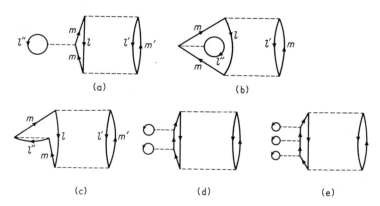

Fɪɢ. 10. Members of a series of graphs whose effect is to replace the kinetic energy of m in the energy denominator by its Hartree-Fock energy.

fermion line joins the vertex to itself. Each of these extra vertices multiplies the contribution of the graph by

$$(T_l + T_{l'} - T_m - T_{m'})^{-1}(V_{ml'',ml''} - V_{ml'',l''m}).$$

If we sum over all possible hole states l'', this just gives

$$V_m/(T_l + T_{l'} - T_m - T_{m'}),$$

where V_m is a matrix element of the Hartree-Fock potential which appears in Eq. (3.7). If we add all graphs like those in Fig. 10 to the graph of Fig. 6(a), we get an infinite geometric series. The sum of this series is obtained by changing the T_m in the energy denominator to the Hartree-Fock energy

$$\epsilon_m = T_m + V_m, \tag{4.39}$$

provided that $T_m + T_{m'} - T_l - T_{l'} > |V_m|$, so that the series converges. This inequality is not satisfied for all choices of l, l', m, and m', so that this partial series must diverge in some cases. This does not necessarily mean that the whole perturbation series diverges, but it does suggest that it is better to include the Hartree-Fock energies in the unperturbed Hamiltonian.

This can be done by adding the Hartree-Fock energy to the unperturbed Hamiltonian and subtracting it from the perturbation, so that we have

$$H_0 = \sum_k (T_k + V_k)a_k{}^\dagger a_k,$$

$$H_1 = \tfrac{1}{2}\sum V_{k_1k_2,k_3k_4}a_{k_2}{}^\dagger a_{k_1}{}^\dagger a_{k_3}a_{k_4} - \sum_k V_k a_k{}^\dagger a_k. \tag{4.40}$$

The new element in the perturbation is represented by a dotted horizontal line with a fermion line entering and leaving at one end. We draw a cross at the other end. Examples of graphs which contain this are shown in Fig. 11. Graphs like Fig. 11(b) exactly cancel graphs like Figs. 10(a), (b), and (c), and only the first order graph, Fig. 11(a), does not cancel with a corresponding graph of this sort. Figure 11(a) added to Fig. 5 changes the "unperturbed" energy $\sum_k(T_k + V_k)$ to

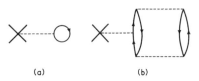

(a)   (b)

Fig. 11. Additional graphs that occur when the Hartree-Fock energy is included in the unperturbed Hamiltonian.

the value $\sum_k (T_k + \frac{1}{2}V_k)$ given in Eq. (3.8). The corrections to this value are found by drawing all linked graphs according to the rules of Sec. 5, but excluding any graph in which a fermion line joins two points at the same level, since such graphs are cancelled by corresponding graphs containing this new type of interaction. The same rule applies if the solution of the Hartree-Fock equations is something other than a determinant of plane waves, provided that this solution is used as the basis for the representation.

7. Brueckner theory

Brueckner's theory of nuclear structure is an attempt to overcome the difficulties created by the strong forces which act between nucleons. Analysis of nucleon-nucleon scattering data has shown that there is a strong repulsion at short distances, which can be adequately represented as an infinitely positive potential (hard core) for nucleon separations less than 0.5×10^{-13} cm. As we observed in the previous chapter, the expectation value of such a potential is infinite for a determinant of plane waves, yet we should not expect a very small repulsive core to make much difference to the structure of a nucleus. It is the scattering data at high energies only (100 to 300 Mev) that shows the existence of the hard core, and we expect the general features of nuclear structure to depend more on those characteristics of the potential which determine low energy scattering.

The theory was originally suggested by the work of Watson and his collaborators on the theory of the scattering of particles from complex nuclei (Watson, 1953; Francis and Watson, 1953; Watson, 1957). This work has shown that, to a first approximation, the scattering is an additive effect to which all the nucleons in the nucleus contribute independently. In the original paper of Brueckner and Watson (1953), an attempt was made to relate nuclear binding to the interaction between pions and nucleons. The pions were pictured as moving through the nucleus, and being scattered or absorbed by successive nucleons. In later papers, these virtual pions have not been considered, and in the paper by Brueckner, *et al.* (1954) the nucleons are regarded as scattering from one another. These authors were able to find an expression for the binding energy of nuclear matter in terms of the nucleon-nucleon scattering phase shifts, but the results were not satisfactory. The analysis of Brueckner and Levinson (1955) suggested that, since the scatterings take place in nuclear matter rather than in a vacuum, two effects modify the scattering process. Firstly, the nucleons move in a potential due to all the other nucleons, so that they have a sort of Hartree-Fock energy rather than just a kinetic energy; the calculation of this effect is referred to as the self-consistency problem. Secondly, neither nucleon can scatter into an intermediate state which is already occupied, but both nucleons must go into unoccupied states; the calculation of this effect is referred to as the problem of the exclusion principle in intermediate states. The most complete discussion of this approach has been given by Bethe (1956), where references are given to some of the early papers not mentioned here. A careful calculation of the energy and density of nuclear matter has now been made by Brueckner and Gammel (1958a), and remarkable agreement with experiment is obtained.

The original derivation of Brueckner theory from the theory of multiple scattering (Brueckner and associates, 1954) gives a simple picture of nuclear matter, but the corrections suggested by Brueckner and Levinson (1955) lead to a lot of complication and ambiguities. The problems involved in making these corrections are much clearer when expressed in the language of perturbation theory than they are in the language of scattering theory. The formalisms of Goldstone (1957) and Hugenholtz (1957) were developed to study these problems.

These papers start from the observation that the Hartree-Fock ground state energy is a sum of graphs like Figs. 5(a), 5(b), and 11(a) added to the unperturbed ground state energy. Since Figs. 5(a) and (b) give an infinite contribution for a hard core potential, we also take into account the infinite series of graphs whose first few members are shown in Fig. 12. We include in this series also the exchange terms, so that Fig. 12(a) should really be replaced by the four graphs of Fig. 6. This infinite series, including the contributions from Fig. 5, is

$$W_1 = \sum_l \sum_{l'} \{ \tfrac{1}{2}(V_{ll',ll'} - V_{ll',l'l}) + \tfrac{1}{4} \sum_m \sum_{m'} |V_{ll',mm'} - V_{ll',m'm}|^2$$
$$\times (\epsilon_l + \epsilon_{l'} - \epsilon_m - \epsilon_{m'})^{-1} + \tfrac{1}{8} \sum_m \sum_{m'} \sum_{m''} \sum_{m'''} (V_{ll',mm'} - V_{ll',m'm})$$
$$\times (\epsilon_l + \epsilon_{l'} - \epsilon_m - \epsilon_{m'})(V_{mm',m''m'''} - V_{mm',m'''m''})(\epsilon_l + \epsilon_{l'} - \epsilon_{m''} - \epsilon_{m'''})^{-1}$$
$$\times (V_{m''m''',ll'} - V_{m''m''',l'l}) + \cdots \}, \quad (4.41)$$

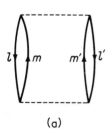 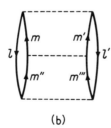 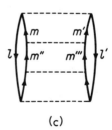

(a)   (b)   (c)

FIG. 12. Graphs that contribute to the ground state energy in Brueckner theory.

where ϵ_k is the unperturbed energy of the single-particle state k. The sums on l and l' go over all occupied states, and the sums on m, m', m'', and m''' go over all unoccupied states. The graphs chosen allow for the excitation of only one pair of particles, which can then interact with one another any number of times so long as they remain in unoccupied states. This formula takes account of the exclusion principle in intermediate states. We define a matrix K in the space of two-particle states by

$$K_{kk',ll'} = (V_{kk',ll'} - V_{kk',l'l}) + \tfrac{1}{2} \sum_{m>k_F} \sum_{m'>k_F} (V_{kk',mm'} - V_{kk',m'm})$$

$$\times (\epsilon_l + \epsilon_{l'} - \epsilon_m - \epsilon_{m'})^{-1} K_{mm',ll'}. \quad (4.42)$$

Iteration of this equation shows that the quantity in the curly brackets of Eq. (4.41) is $\tfrac{1}{2} K_{ll',ll'}$. The energy shift is

$$W_1 = \tfrac{1}{2} \sum_{l<k_F} \sum_{l'<k_F} K_{ll',ll'}. \quad (4.43)$$

The equation (4.42) which defines the matrix K is like a two-body scattering equation, and so K is sometimes called the reaction matrix; it is also called the G-matrix or t-matrix in various papers, but we shall refer to it as the K-matrix. It is not a scattering equation because the ϵ's which appear in the denominator are self-consistent energies (in a sense described in the next paragraph) rather than kinetic energies, and because the sum over intermediate states is restricted to levels outside the Fermi sea. It should be noticed that the energy denominator never vanishes, but is always negative. The great virtue of this method is that even for a hard core potential K has finite matrix elements in momentum space, just as the scattering matrix does in scattering theory. The solution of Eq. (4.42), which is generally called the Bethe-Goldstone equation, has been discussed for the case of a hard core potential by Bethe and Goldstone (1957) and by Brueckner and Wada (1956). We can write the equation formally as a matrix equation

$$K = V + V\frac{P}{e}K, \quad (4.44)$$

where P is a projection operator which excludes occupied states and e is the energy denominator. If φ is the two-particle state consisting of plane waves with momenta l and l', so that we have $e\varphi = 0$, the equation for $\psi = V^{-1}K\varphi$ is

$$e\psi = e\varphi + PK\varphi = PV\psi, \quad (4.45)$$

which is very like a Schrödinger equation (with a nonlocal potential)

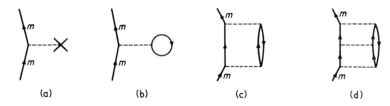

FIG. 13. A series of elements that should cancel if the particle energy is chosen self-consistently in Brueckner theory.

for two particles. This equation can be written in configuration space and solved by the usual methods.

The self-consistency problem is treated in the same spirit. In the Hartree-Fock theory, the self-consistent potential is chosen so that every graph which includes a part like Fig. 13(a) is exactly cancelled by a corresponding graph with a part like Fig. 13(b). Figure 13(b) gives an infinite factor with a hard core potential, so we include also the infinite series of parts like Figs. 13(c) and (d). The particle m is allowed to excite one particle from the medium, and then to interact with it any number of times before it returns to its initial state. For a hole state, the graphs which are cancelled contain the infinite series of parts which are like those shown in Fig. 14. Such graphs take account of the fact that the absence of a particle from the state l prevents its excitation. The sum of such graphs is given by the sum of diagonal elements of the K-matrix, so that the self-consistent energy is

$$\epsilon_k = T_k + \sum_{l<k_F} K_{kl,kl}. \tag{4.46}$$

The coupling of Eqs. (4.42) and (4.46) to one another makes the problem of calculating the K-matrix very difficult, and the methods used for obtaining the solution are discussed by Brueckner and Gammel (1958a). The importance of self-consistency can be estimated by examining higher order terms in the expansion of the energy in powers of K (Thouless, 1958).

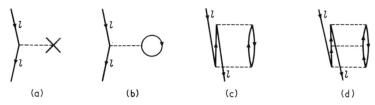

FIG. 14. A series of elements that should cancel if the hole energy is chosen self-consistently in Brueckner theory.

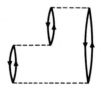

FIG. 15. A three-body cluster.

It is only for short-range potentials that the Brueckner theory is any better than simple perturbation theory. It includes all second-order terms, but calculations by Swiatecki (1956) and Thouless (1957a) show that the second-order term would only contribute about 1 Mev per particle at nuclear densities if the potential were a Yukawa potential with an exchange mixture (the kinetic energy is about 23 Mev per particle, and the potential energy about -39 Mev per particle). Unless the range of the force is much less than the particle separation, there is no reason to suppose that third-order graphs like Fig. 12(b) are any more important than graphs like Fig. 15, which are called three-body clusters because they involve the excitation of three particles from the Fermi sea.

Without making the detailed calculations of Brueckner and Gammel (1958a), Gomes and co-workers (1958) have used this method to study the properties of nuclear matter. They find that ψ should only differ from φ of Eq. (4.45) when the nucleons are quite close to one another, and they call the distance at which the two wave functions become almost identical the *healing distance*. The healing distance is much reduced by the effect of the exclusion principle. In a paper by De-Shalit and Weisskopf (1958) it is shown that corrections to the Brueckner theory should be small. Low energy properties of a nucleus should not depend critically in what happens inside the healing distance; this is regarded as the explanation of the success of the shell model. This argument is less certain in the surface region of the nucleus, since there the exclusion principle has less effect, and there may be important corrections to the Brueckner theory.

Although the hard core does not make the shell model invalid for certain calculations, such as the calculation of magnetic moments (Amado, 1958), there are some effects which cannot be explained by the simple shell model, and whose existence is good evidence for correlations in the nucleus due to the hard core. These are high energy processes which depend on the existence of highly excited nucleons in the ground state of the nucleus. For example, the absorption of a high-energy photon by the nucleus can only occur if there are two correlated nucleons to take up the energy of the photon, but this process does occur readily. The evidence for such correlations has been analysed by Brueckner *et al.* (1955).

For nuclear matter, the core radius is about 0.5×10^{-13} cm, while the particle density is $(\frac{4}{3}\pi r_0^3)^{-1}$, where r_0 is 1.1×10^{-13} cm. For liquid He^3, the core radius (the diameter of an atom) is about 2.5×10^{-8} cm, while r_0 is 2.33×10^{-8} cm, so it is not surprising that the calculation of the properties of liquid He^3 by this method (Brueckner and Gammel, 1958b) gives less satisfactory results than the calculation of the properties of nuclear matter. Qualitatively, however, liquid He^3 appears to be similar to nuclear matter, since its density is much less than the density we should expect for a classical liquid with the same interatomic forces. The saturation density is determined by the balance between the attractive part of the potential on the one hand, and the kinetic energy and the repulsive part on the other. Brueckner theory enables such problems to be handled, since the rapidly varying potential V is replaced by the smoothly varying matrix K.

8. Brueckner theory for finite nuclei

The results of the calculation of the K-matrix for nuclear matter at various densities can be used to calculate the structure of finite nuclei (Brueckner and associates, 1958). It is found that when the K-matrix is written in configuration space, it differs from the potential V only for distances between the two interacting particles less than 10^{-13} cm (this is then the healing distance). At these short distances, V is local but varies very rapidly, while K is nonlocal and dependent on density, but is slowly varying, quite suitable for a Hartree-Fock type of calculation. Now, although the density of an actual nucleus varies greatly over a distance equal to the range of the potential, so that attempts to apply the Thomas-Fermi method have been unsuccessful, the density does not vary much over the distance 10^{-13} cm for which the density dependence of the K-matrix is important. According to Eq. (4.43), the potential energy of the ground state is equal to a sum of diagonal elements of the K-matrix, just as in the Hartree-Fock theory it is a sum of diagonal elements of the potential. Although K ought to be defined by an equation like Eq. (4.42), where the sum over intermediate states goes over all levels not occupied in the particular finite nucleus, it is reasonable to assume that the K-matrix depends only on the local density, because of the short range of its density-dependent part. Thus the calculation is, in a sense, a combination of the Hartree-Fock method and the Thomas-Fermi method.

The use of this variational method has been described by Brueckner and Goldman (1959). With a particular choice of trial wave functions, the expectation value of the ground state energy is

$$E_0 = -(\hbar^2/2M) \sum_{i=1}^{A} \int \psi_i^*(r) \nabla^2 \psi_i(r) d^3r$$

$$+ \tfrac{1}{2} \sum_{i=1}^{A} \sum_{j=1}^{A} \iiiint \psi_i^*(r_1) \psi_j^*(r_2) K^{(\rho)}(r_1, r_2; r_3, r_4) \psi_i(r_3) \psi_j(r_4) d^3r_1 d^3r_2 d^3r_3 d^3r_4.$$

$$(4.47)$$

There is no need to put in the exchange term, since in Eq. (4.42) we defined K to be antisymmetric. The density ρ on which K depends is taken to be the particle density at the point $\tfrac{1}{4}(r_1 + r_2 + r_3 + r_4)$. We now have to choose the single-particle wave functions so that the expression (4.47) is minimized. Variation of the wave functions in this equation leads to

$$-(\hbar^2/2M) \nabla^2 \psi_i(r)$$

$$+ \sum_{j=1}^{A} \iiint \psi_j^*(r_1) K^{(\rho)}(r, r_1; r', r_2) \psi_j(r_2) \psi_i(r') d^3r_1 d^3r_2 d^3r'$$

$$+ \tfrac{1}{2} \sum_{j=1}^{A} \sum_{k=1}^{A} \iiiint \psi_j^*(r_1) \psi_k^*(r_2) K'^{(\rho)}(r_1, r_2; r_3, r_4) \psi_j(r_3) \psi_k(r_4)$$

$$\times \delta[\tfrac{1}{4}(\mathbf{r_1} + \mathbf{r_2} + \mathbf{r_3} + \mathbf{r_4}) - \mathbf{r}] d^3r_1 d^3r_2 d^3r_3 d^3r_4 \psi_i(r) = \epsilon_i \psi_i(r). \quad (4.48)$$

The first two terms on the left of this equation are similar to the terms of the Hartree-Fock theory in Eq. (3.11). The third term on the left is a new term, which comes from the dependence of the K-matrix on density; $K'^{(\rho)}$ denotes the derivative of the matrix $K^{(\rho)}$ with respect to density. This part of the potential energy of a single-particle state is called the *rearrangement energy*. The reason for this name is that the K-matrix includes some of the effects of correlations between the particles. When the density changes, the particles rearrange themselves, and so the K-matrix changes.

The definition of single-particle energy levels ϵ_i by Eq. (4.48) is more satisfactory than the definition by Eq. (4.46), which does not include the rearrangement energy, since the energies of excited states are given correctly. In particular, the theorem of Bethe (1956) and Hugenholtz and Van Hove (1958) that the energy of a particle on the Fermi surface must equal the average energy of all the particles in the system is satisfied. The energy of a particle on the Fermi surface is the extra energy which would be obtained by adding one particle to the system without changing its volume, while the average energy is the extra energy which would be obtained by adding one particle to the system without changing its density. These two quantities must be equal if the system is in equilibrium at zero pressure. The rearrangement energy is discussed in general terms by Thouless (1958), and is evaluated for nuclear matter by Brueckner and associates (1960a). One effect of the rearrangement energy is that the relation (3.8) between the total energy and the kinetic and single-particle energies no longer holds. This relation is valid if the single-particle energies are defined by Eq. (4.46), as can be seen from Eq. (4.43).

Calculations using this method have been carried out for closed shell nuclei, with moderately satisfactory results (Brueckner, *et al.*, 1961). Objections to this method have been raised by Eden *et al.* (1959). They argue that the wave functions in Eq. (4.47) should be varied with K kept fixed, so that the rearrangement energy should not occur in Eq. (4.48). Calculations made without this term agree less well with experiment.

9. Divergence of the K-matrix

Although calculations of the K-matrix have been successful, it is possible that it may diverge for certain values of the momentum. This was shown by De Dominicis (1957), who solved Eq. (4.42) for a separable potential. A separable potential is one whose matrix elements are equal to a product of a function of the initial state and a function of the final state, if the initial and final states have the same total momentum, so that we have

$$V_{kk',k''k'''} = -v^*(k, k')v(k'', k''')\delta_{k+k',k''+k'''}. \qquad (4.49)$$

The equation for K becomes

$$K_{mm',ll'}$$
$$= -v^*(m, m')v(l, l')\delta_{m+m',l+l'} - \tfrac{1}{2}\sum_{m''>k_F}\sum_{m'''>k_F} v^*(m, m')v(m'', m''')$$
$$\times \delta_{m+m',m''+m'''}(\epsilon_l + \epsilon_{l'} - \epsilon_{m''} - \epsilon_{m'''})^{-1}K_{m''m''',ll'}. \qquad (4.50)$$

We can multiply this by $v(m, m')(\epsilon_l + \epsilon_{l'} - \epsilon_m - \epsilon_{m'})^{-1}$ and sum over m and m' to get a single linear equation whose solution is

$$\sum_{m>k_F}\sum_{m'>k_F} v(m, m')(\epsilon_l + \epsilon_{l'} - \epsilon_m - \epsilon_{m'})^{-1}K_{mm',ll'}$$
$$= 2v(l, l')X(l, l')/[1 - X(l, l')], \qquad (4.51)$$

where

$$X(l, l') = \tfrac{1}{2}\sum_{m>k_F}\sum_{m'>k_F} |v(m, m')|^2(\epsilon_m + \epsilon_{m'} - \epsilon_l - \epsilon_{l'})^{-1}\delta_{m+m',l+l'}.$$

$$(4.52)$$

Equation (4.51) can be substituted back into Eq. (4.50) to get

$$K_{mm',ll'} = -v^*(m, m')v(l, l')\delta_{m+m',l+l'}/[1 - X(l, l')].   (4.53).$$

It is easy to show that X gets indefinitely large as l and l' approach the Fermi surface at opposite ends of a diameter. We take the momenta of l and l' to be opposite, so that m and m' are also opposite. The part of the sum on the right of Eq. (4.52) which gives rise to the divergence is the part which comes from m and m' very close to the Fermi surface. In this region, we can put $|v(m, m')|^2$ equal to a constant (unless it goes to zero at the Fermi surface, in which case this argument is no longer valid), and the energy denominator is equal to some constant times $m - l$. The number of states in a particular energy range varies only slowly, and so the sum on the right of Eq. (4.52) is proportional to $-\log (k_F - l)$ when l is very close to k_F. The sum is always positive, and is quite small away from the Fermi surface, so it must go through unity at some point. If X is unity, Eq. (4.53) shows that the K-matrix is infinite.

A similar divergence should occur for other attractive potentials, not necessarily separable. It is now known that this divergence is closely connected with the "superfluidity" of nuclear matter, and we consider it further when we discuss the theory of superconductivity. A numerical solution of Eq. (4.42) is unlikely to reveal the divergence, since it is important only very close to the Fermi surface.

A fuller discussion of Brueckner theory and its applications to nuclear matter and liquid He³ has been given by Brueckner in his lectures at the summer school at Les Houches of 1958.* The lectures of Hugenholtz, Thouless, and Weisskopf are also concerned with matters discussed in this chapter.

* Published in "The Many-Body Problem," Methuen, London, 1959.

V. Low-Lying Excited States

1. Green's functions and collective variables

In the previous two chapters we have been concerned with methods of determining the energy and other properties of the ground state of a many-body system. There are difficulties in studying the excited states of a many-particle system which do not usually arise in the quantum mechanics of a single particle. There are so many ways of exciting a many-particle system that the excited states overlap. If the lifetime of an excited state is so short that the uncertainty in its energy is greater than its distance from neighbouring excited states, it can hardly be called a stationary state. Also, perturbation theory in its usual form cannot be applied to states which are nearly degenerate, since the energy denominators get very small.

Fortunately, a complete knowledge of the excited states of a complicated system is not required. The lowest excited states of atoms and nuclei are observable, and their energies and lifetimes can be measured, but extended systems, such as solids and liquids, usually have excited states with energies going continuously down to the ground state energy. It is more important to know what excited states are reached by altering the levels of one or two particles in the ground state than to have a complete description of a particular excited state. Many important physical properties of the system can be accurately calculated by use of second order perturbation theory if the excited states reached in this way are known. Properties for which this is true are the electric polarizability, the magnetic susceptibility, and the attenuation of light or sound. For example, the electric polarizability can be obtained from the quantity

$$\sum_n |V_{0n}|^2 (E_0 - E_n)^{-1},$$

where V_{0n} is the matrix element of the applied electrostatic potential between the ground state of the system and the excited state of energy

E_n. The electrostatic potential is a single-particle operator, and has matrix elements only between configurations which differ in the level of a single particle.

The functions which are called *Green's functions* give a complete description of what states are reached by altering the levels of one or two particles, and so they are very closely related to physically observable quantities. There are two problems with which we are concerned. One problem is to find what mathematical properties the Green's functions must have, and what is the relation between the Green's functions and the physical properties of the system. The mathematical properties of the Green's functions are very important, and lead to the *dispersion relations* or *sum rules*. The second problem is to calculate the Green's functions from the interactions between the particles, and for this we use perturbation theory. These two problems are not distinct, and we have to keep both in mind at the same time.

There is another method of studying excited states which appears to be very different from the Green's function method. There are operators which commute with the Hamiltonian of the system, so that the corresponding physical variables are conserved. For example, the total momentum of a system is such a variable, and we call it a *collective variable*. There are other collective variables which are only approximately conserved, and these are usually more interesting. There are excited states which differ from the ground state only because the collective variables have different values, and, if the system is in such a state, we say that it has a *collective* excitation but no *intrinsic* excitation. Appropriate collective variables are often suggested by the analogy with classical systems; for example, the classical analogy suggests that a nucleus with a spheroidal shape should be able to have a rotational collective motion. The relation between the Green's function method and the collective variable method is discussed in some detail.

Further useful information about the energy levels of an extended system can be obtained from the thermodynamic properties of the system. The properties of a system at finite temperatures are determined by the average properties of energy levels with a certain mean energy. We discuss methods of calculating thermodynamic properties in Chapters VI, VII, and VIII.

2. One-particle Green's functions

We consider an extended system, for which the ground state wave function $|\Psi_0\rangle$ is an eigenstate of momentum with eigenvalue zero. The one-particle Green's function is defined as

$$S_k(t_1 - t_2) = \langle \Psi_0| T[a_k(t_2) a_k{}^\dagger(t_1)]|\Psi_0\rangle, \qquad (5.1)$$

where

$$a_k(t) = \exp(iHt) a_k \exp(-iHt). \qquad (5.2)$$

It must be noticed that the time dependence of the annihilation and creation operators is defined in terms of the true Hamiltonian of the system, whereas in Eq. (4.15) we defined the time dependence in terms of an unperturbed Hamiltonian. In this chapter we use the Heisenberg picture instead of the interaction picture. The operators $a_k{}^\dagger$ and a_k create and destroy a particle with momentum k and some particular spin. It is possible to define a Green's function in which the creation and annihilation operators do not refer to the same level, but this vanishes for an extended system, because $|\Psi_0\rangle$ is an eigenstate of total momentum and total spin. For a finite system, it may be convenient to use some other set of creation and annihilation operators, and then the single-particle Green's function does not vanish if the creation and annihilation operators on the right of Eq. (5.1) are different from one another. We use the equation $H|\Psi_0\rangle = E_0|\Psi_0\rangle$ and the definition of the time-ordered product to get

$$S_k(t_1 - t_2) \begin{cases} = \langle\Psi_0|a_k \exp[i(H - E_0)(t_1 - t_2)] a_k{}^\dagger|\Psi_0\rangle, & \text{for } t_1 < t_2, \\ = -\langle\Psi_0|a_k{}^\dagger \exp[-i(H - E_0)(t_1 - t_2)] a_k|\Psi_0\rangle, & \text{for } t_1 \geq t_2. \end{cases}$$
$$(5.3)$$

If we have $H = H_0$, so that $|\Psi_0\rangle = |\Phi_0\rangle$, this definition is identical to the definition of the contracted product of the operators a_k and $a_k{}^\dagger$ given by Eqs. (4.28) and (4.29). We refer to this function as the *true propagator* of the level k, as opposed to the unperturbed propagator defined earlier. Suppose that we add a particle of momentum k to the ground state at time t_1, allow the state formed to develop freely until a later time t_2, and then remove a particle with momentum k. The scalar product of the state we obtain in this way with the ground state is equal to $S_k(t_1 - t_2)$, according to Eq. (5.3). For $t_1 \geq t_2$, we have first to remove a particle of momentum k at time t_2, and then replace it at t_1.

The expectation value of any single-particle operator can be obtained immediately from the single-particle Green's functions. The average number of particles in the level k is, from Eq. (5.3),

$$\langle n_k\rangle = -\lim_{t \to +0} S_k(t). \qquad (5.4)$$

This formula allows us to calculate the expectation value of any single-particle operator. In particular, the kinetic energy operator has expectation value

$$\langle T \rangle = \sum_k (\hbar^2 k^2/2M) \langle n_k \rangle = -\lim_{t \to +0} \sum_k (\hbar^2 k^2/2M) S_k(t). \quad (5.5)$$

The expectation value of the potential energy can also be found, since we have

$$\lim_{t \to +0} dS_k(t)/dt = i \langle \Psi_0 | a_k^\dagger (H - E_0) a_k | \Psi_0 \rangle$$

$$= -i \langle \Psi_0 | [H, a_k^\dagger] a_k | \Psi_0 \rangle. \quad (5.6)$$

If we have

$$H = T + V = \sum_k T_k a_k^\dagger a_k + \tfrac{1}{2} \sum_k \sum_{k'} \sum_{k''} \sum_{k'''} V_{kk',k''k'''} a_{k'}^\dagger a_k^\dagger a_{k''} a_{k'''},$$

then the commutator is

$$(5.7)$$

$$[H, a_k^\dagger] = T_k a_k^\dagger + \tfrac{1}{2} \sum_{k'} \sum_{k''} \sum_{k'''} (V_{k'k'',k'''k} - V_{k'k'',kk'''}) a_{k''}^\dagger a_{k'}^\dagger a_{k'''}.$$

$$(5.8)$$

Substitution of this in Eq. (5.6) gives the result

$$\lim_{t \to +0} \sum_k dS_k(t)/dt = -i\langle T \rangle - 2i \langle V \rangle. \quad (5.9)$$

Combination of this result with Eq. (5.5) enables us to find E_0, the expectation value of the Hamiltonian, which is

$$E_0 = \tfrac{1}{2} \lim_{t \to +0} \sum_k \left[\frac{\hbar^2 k^2}{2M} S_k(t) + i \frac{dS_k(t)}{dt} \right]. \quad (5.10)$$

If the interaction had only diagonal elements, so that the Hartree-Fock energies were exact, this formula would be the same as Eq. (3.8).

Another relation satisfied by the single-particle Green's function follows from the anticommutation relation of a_k and $a_k^\dagger$. This is

$$\lim_{t \to +0} [S_k(-t) - S_k(t)] = \langle \Psi_0 | (a_k a_k^\dagger + a_k^\dagger a_k) | \Psi_0 \rangle = 1. \quad (5.11)$$

The two sum rules (5.10) and (5.11) were derived by Galitskii and Migdal (1958). Most of the other results discussed in this section are to be found in their paper.

We find the dispersion relations satisfied by the Green's functions by studying their Fourier transforms. It is convenient to use the same letter to denote a function and its Fourier transform, distinguishing between the two by the letter used for the argument of the function. Any function of the real variable t can be written as

$$f(t) = f^{(a)}(t) + f^{(r)}(t), \quad (5.12)$$

where the advanced part $f^{(a)}(t)$ vanishes for $t < 0$, while the retarded part $f^{(r)}(t)$ vanishes for $t \geq 0$. We can define the Fourier transform of the advanced part in the lower half plane by

$$f^{(a)}(z) = i \int_0^\infty f(t) \exp(-izt) dt$$

$$= i \int_{-\infty}^\infty f^{(a)}(t) \exp(-izt) dt, \qquad (5.13)$$

and the Fourier transform of the retarded part in the upper half plane by

$$f^{(r)}(z) = i \int_{-\infty}^0 f(t) \exp(-izt) dt$$

$$= i \int_{-\infty}^\infty f^{(r)}(t) \exp(-izt) dt. \qquad (5.14)$$

According to Eq. (5.3), the Fourier transforms of the retarded and advanced parts of $S_k(t)$ are given by

$$S_k^{(r)}(z) = \langle \Psi_0 | a_k (H - E_0 - z)^{-1} a_k^\dagger | \Psi_0 \rangle,$$

$$S_k^{(a)}(z) = -\langle \Psi_0 | a_k^\dagger (H - E_0 + z)^{-1} a_k | \Psi_0 \rangle. \qquad (5.15)$$

In order to study these two functions, we assume that the medium is not infinite, but is enclosed in a finite volume. We impose periodic boundary conditions, so that momentum is still conserved. The eigenvalues of the Hamiltonian for a particular number of particles are now discrete instead of continuous. As the volume increases, we expect the eigenvalues to close up on one another, so that they become continuous in the limit of an infinite volume. We shall also have to assume that we can neglect eigenvalues above a certain limiting value, so that $S_k^{(r)}(z) + S_k^{(a)}(z)$ tends to zero like $-1/z$ for large z.

We can expand Eq. (5.15) as a sum over the eigenstates of the Hamiltonian. The intermediate states for the retarded function have $N + 1$ particles, and we call the eigenvalues $E_n^{(N+1)}$, while the intermediate states for the advanced function have $N - 1$ particles, and we call the eigenvalues $E_n^{(N-1)}$; N is the number of particles in $|\Psi_0\rangle$. The expansion gives

$$S_k^{(r)}(z) = \sum_n |(a_k^\dagger)_{n0}|^2 (E_n^{(N+1)} - E_0^{(N)} - z)^{-1},$$

$$S_k^{(a)}(z) = -\sum_n |(a_k^\dagger)_{0n}|^2 (E_n^{(N-1)} - E_0^{(N)} + z)^{-1}. \qquad (5.16)$$

These two functions were originally defined only in one half plane each, but Eq. (5.16) allows the functions to be analytically continued into the other half plane. It is clear from Eq. (5.16) that we have

$$S_k(z^*) \;=\; S_k^{(r)}(z^*) \;+\; S_k^{(a)}(z^*) \;=\; S_k^*(z). \qquad (5.17)$$

The poles of $S_k^{(r)}(z)$ lie on the real axis above $z = \mu(N) = E_0^{(N+1)} - E_0^{(N)}$, while the poles of $S_k^{(a)}(z)$ lie on the real axis below $z = \mu(N-1) = E_0^{(N)} - E_0^{(N-1)}$. The functions are analytic everywhere else.

As the number of particles increases while the density remains constant, the eigenvalues of the Hamiltonian get closer together. Although the singularities of $S_k(z)$ are indefinitely close together, the function remains analytic off the real axis even for an infinite system. We define the value of the functions on the real axis by

$$S_k^{(r)}(x) \;=\; \lim_{y \to +0} S_k^{(r)}(x + iy),$$

$$S_k^{(a)}(x) \;=\; \lim_{y \to +0} S_k^{(a)}(x - iy). \qquad (5.18)$$

We have to make a cut just below the real axis from $\mu(N)$ to plus infinity, and a cut just below the real axis from $\mu(N - 1)$ to minus infinity, as shown in Fig. 16. From Eq. (5.17) it is clear that the real part of $S_k(z)$ is continuous across the cuts, but the imaginary part is discontinuous unless it is zero. By integrating $S_k^{(r)}(z)$ round the contour C_r which runs along the real axis from minus infinity to plus infinity and is closed by a semicircle in the upper half plane, and by integrating $S_k^{(a)}(z)$ round the contour C_a which runs along the real axis and is closed by an infinite semicircle in the lower half plane, we can get the dispersion relations. Since $S_k(z)$ behaves like $-1/z$ at infinity, we get

$$\int_{-\infty}^{\infty} \big[S_k^{(r)}(x) - S_k^{(a)}(x) \big] dx - \pi i$$

$$= \int_{C_r} S_k^{(r)}(z)\,dz - \int_{C_a} S_k^{(a)}(z)\,dz = 0, \qquad (5.19)$$

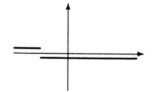

FIG. 16. Cuts that are made in order to define the value of the one-particle Green's function on the real axis.

which is equivalent to Eq. (5.11). In the same way, we can get the relations

$$\int_{-\infty}^{\infty} \frac{S_k^{(r)}(x')}{x'-z}dx' = \begin{cases} 2\pi i S_k^{(r)}(z), & \text{for } \operatorname{Im} z > 0, \\ 0, & \text{for } \operatorname{Im} z < 0, \end{cases}$$

$$\int_{-\infty}^{\infty} \frac{S_k^{(a)}(x')}{x'-z}dx' = \begin{cases} 0, & \text{for } \operatorname{Im} z > 0, \\ -2\pi i S_k^{(a)}(z), & \text{for } \operatorname{Im} z < 0. \end{cases} \tag{5.20}$$

Equations (5.19) and (5.20) give the most important dispersion relations satisfied by $S_k(z)$. The imaginary part of $S_k^{(r)}(z)$ is positive in the upper half plane, and so also on the real axis, while the imaginary part of $S_k^{(a)}(z)$ is negative in the lower half plane, and so also on the real axis, as can be seen from Eqs. (5.15) and (5.18). We can define the *strength function* $g_k(x)$ by

$$g_k(x) = g_k^{(r)}(x) + g_k^{(a)}(x),$$

$$g_k^{(r)}(x) = \pi^{-1} \operatorname{Im} S_k^{(r)}(x) = \sum_n |(a_k^\dagger)_{n0}|^2 \delta(x - E_n^{(N+1)} + E_0^{(N)}),$$

$$g_k^{(a)}(x) = -\pi^{-1} \operatorname{Im} S_k^{(a)}(x) = \sum_n |(a_k^\dagger)_{0n}|^2 \delta(x + E_n^{(N-1)} - E_0^{(N)}).$$

$$\tag{5.21}$$

The strength function gives the distribution of excitation energies (measured from $E_0^{(N)}$) in the states $a_k^\dagger |\Psi_0\rangle$ and $a_k |\Psi_0\rangle$. We can take the imaginary parts of Eqs. (5.19) and (5.20) to get

$$\int_{-\infty}^{\infty} g_k(x)\,dx = 1, \tag{5.22}$$

and

$$P \int_{-\infty}^{\infty} g_k(x')(x'-x)^{-1}dx' = 2\operatorname{Re} S_k(x). \tag{5.23}$$

The advanced and retarded parts of the strength function therefore completely determine the Green's function. If we know only the total strength function, and do not know its advanced and retarded parts separately, we can use the dispersion relations (5.20) to calculate the Green's function everywhere except on the real axis.

3. Perturbation calculation of Green's functions

We can calculate Green's functions by the methods developed in the previous chapter. In order to calculate the quantity

$$\langle \Phi_0 | U(t_2' - t_2) a_k U(t_2 - t_1) a_k^\dagger U(t_1 - t_1') | \Phi_0 \rangle,$$

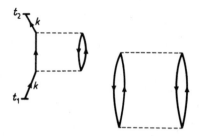

FIG. 17. An unlinked graph with an external line.

where $t_2' > t_2 > t_1 > t_1$, we can use Wick's theorem. We have to draw a line k entering the graph at time t_1, and a line k leaving the graph at time t_2, to represent the operators $a_k^\dagger$ and a_k respectively. The perturbation expansion of the development operators is represented by any number of vertices between t_1' and t_2', so that the process of contraction gives graphs like the ground state graphs, except that there is a single external line. Figures 13 and 14 show some such graphs, and others are shown in Figs. 17 and 18. These graphs can be either linked or unlinked; in the latter case they consist of a part linked to the external line, and some unlinked parts which have no external lines attached to them. An example of a graph with one unlinked part is shown in Fig. 17. The unlinked parts, however, are just the graphs which give $\langle \Phi | U(t_2' - t_1') | \Phi_0 \rangle$, so that the sum of linked graphs with a single external line gives

$$\langle \Phi_0 | U(t_2' - t_2) a_k U(t_2 - t_1) a_k^\dagger U(t_1 - t_1') | \Phi_0 \rangle / \langle \Phi_0 | U(t_2' - t_1') | \Phi_0 \rangle.$$

In the usual way, we let the imaginary parts of $-t_1'$ and t_2' tend to minus infinity, and this fraction tends to

$$\langle \Psi_0 | \exp(iHt_2) a_k \exp[iH(t_1 - t_2)] a_k^\dagger \exp(-iHt_1) | \Psi_0 \rangle,$$

which is just the retarded part of the Green's function defined by Eq. (5.3). The advanced part can be calculated in the same way, except that the external line must enter the graph above the point at which it leaves. The graphs of Fig. 15 contribute to the retarded part, and the graphs of Fig. 16 to the advanced part.

We can make a further simplification of this calculation. Some graphs can be broken into two parts by breaking a single fermion line. An example of such a graph is shown in Fig. 18(a); this graph can be broken into the two parts shown in Figs. 18(b) and (c). A part which is only joined to the rest of the graph by two fermion lines is called a fermion *self-energy part*; this name was introduced into field theory by Dyson (1949b). A graph which contains no self-energy parts which can be split off in this way is said to be *connected*. The graph of Fig. 18(a) breaks up into two connected parts.

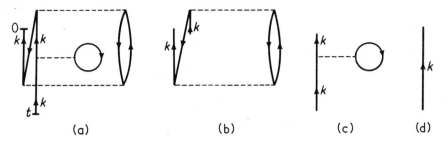

(a)   (b)   (c)   (d)

FIG. 18. The graph shown in (a) can be broken to give the two connected self-energy parts shown in (b) and (c). The simplest graph which contributes to the one-particle Green's function is shown in (d).

We can follow the external line through the graph from the point at which it enters the graph at time t to the point at which it leaves the graph at time 0. Either there is no interaction along this line, in which case the graph must be the one shown in Fig. 18(d) and must contribute only to the unperturbed propagator $S_k^{(0)}(t)$ defined by Eqs. (4.28) and (4.29), or the last interaction along the line must occur at some time t'. If there are some interactions in the graph, there must be one or more connected self-energy parts, and the last connected self-energy part must run from some time t'', at which the first interaction in the self-energy part occurs, to t', at which the last interaction occurs. The first interaction may occur at a later time than the first, since the fermion line may go backwards in time. We call the sum of all connected parts which begin at t'' and end at t', $\Sigma_k(t'' - t')$. Between t and t'', any graph which contributes to $S_k(t - t'')$ can occur. The contribution of all graphs whose last connected part runs from t'' to t' is therefore

$$S_k^{(0)}(t')\Sigma_k(t'' - t')S_k(t - t'').$$

Since t'' and t' can be anywhere, we get an integral equation for $S_k(t)$,

$$S_k(t) = S_k^{(0)}(t) + \int_{-\infty}^{\infty}\int_{-\infty}^{\infty} S_k^{(0)}(t')\Sigma_k(t'' - t')S_k(t - t'')dt'dt''. \tag{5.24}$$

We can take the Fourier transform of this equation, and we get, by use of Eqs. (4.28) and (4.29),

$$S_k(z) = (T_k - z)^{-1} - (T_k - z)^{-1}\Sigma_k(z)S_k(z),$$
$$S_k(z) = [T_k + \Sigma_k(z) - z]^{-1}. \tag{5.25}$$

The rule for calculating $\Sigma_k(z)$ is that all connected self-energy parts with the external line k must be drawn. We can find the contribution of a particular connected graph by the rules of Chapter IV, Sec. 5, if we

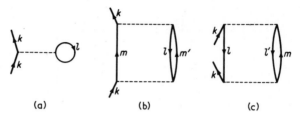

Fig. 19. First and second order connected self-energy parts.

join up the two ends of the external line with a line whose kinetic energy is z rather than T_k; this extra line always counts as a hole line and gives a factor -1. According to this prescription, the contributions of the first and second order graphs shown in Fig. 19 are

$$\tfrac{1}{2} V_{kl,kl},$$

$$\tfrac{1}{4} |V_{kl,mm'}|^2 (z + T_l - T_m - T_{m'})^{-1},$$

and

$$-\tfrac{1}{4} |V_{ll'km}|^2 (T_l + T_{l'} - z - T_m)^{-1}.$$

Therefore, in second order perturbation theory, the value of $\Sigma_k(z)$ is

$$\Sigma_k^{(2)}(z) = \sum_{l<k_F} (V_{kl,kl} - V_{kl,lk})$$

$$+ \tfrac{1}{4} \sum_{l<k_F} \sum_{m,m'>k_F} |V_{kl,mm'} - V_{kl,m'm}|^2 (z + T_l - T_m - T_{m'})^{-1}$$

$$-\tfrac{1}{4} \sum_{l,l'<k_F} \sum_{m>k_F} |V_{ll',km} - V_{ll',mk}|^2 (T_l + T_{l'} - z - T_m)^{-1}. \quad (5.26)$$

The first order graph shown in Fig. 19(a) just gives the Hartree-Fock potential energy, as we discussed in Chapter IV, Sec. 6. The second order graphs alter the form of the propagator, because of their z-dependence, and this has some important effects, which we can most easily discuss by using the strength function defined by Eq. (5.21).

The strength function is found by taking the limit of the imaginary part of the Green's function as its argument approaches the real axis from above. If only the first term on the right of Eq. (5.26) were considered, the strength function would be a δ-function of $z - T_k - \sum_l (V_{kl,kl} - V_{kl,lk})$. The second and third terms alter the behaviour of the strength function, because they have positive imaginary parts in the neighbourhood of the real axis. The denominator of Eq. (5.25) therefore never vanishes, and the strength function is a well-behaved function. It should be noticed that the imaginary parts of z and $\Sigma_k(z)$ have opposite signs, so that $S_k(z)$ is regular everywhere except on the real axis in our approximation. The dispersion relations (5.20) or

(5.23) therefore hold, and so does Eq. (5.22). In order to use sum rules such as Eq. (5.4) or (5.10), it is necessary to know the advanced part of the propagator. This can be most easily found from Eq. (5.24); it can easily be seen that both advanced and retarded self-energy parts contribute to the advanced part of the propagator. Such problems have been analysed in more detail by Prange and Klein (1958) and Thouless (1959).

One of the great advantages of using this sort of method for studying excited states of a system is that the Green's function gives the difference in energy of the ground state and the excited states. It is not necessary to know the ground state energy with great accuracy and to subtract it from the excited state energy to obtain the excitation energy. The removal of the unlinked graphs from the expansion is the step in the argument which is necessary to produce this property. For an infinite system, this is essential, since the ground state energy is proportional to the extent of the system, while we are interested in states excited by an energy which is independent of the energy of the system. There is no doubt, however, that this step makes the convergence of the perturbation series much worse, since we have to divide by a number, the expectation value of the development operator, which is likely to have zeros for quite small values of the coupling constant. It is indeed clear that a power series expansion of Eq. (5.25) in powers of the interaction near $z = T_k$ cannot converge. We hope that the validity of our expressions extends further than the validity of the methods used to derive them, and this can be shown in some cases, but we cannot regard these derivations as rigourous.

4. The optical model

The elastic scattering of neutrons or protons by nuclei can be calculated satisfactorily by the optical model, according to which the nucleus behaves like a potential well. Because inelastic scattering occurs, the potential has to have an imaginary part. The elastic scattering of a single particle by a nucleus in its ground state is clearly described by the retarded part of the one-particle Green's function as defined in Eq. (5.3); the extra particle is created by the operator $a_k{}^\dagger$, and the Green's function describes the way in which it propagates. We consider at first the way in which this extra particle propagates in uniform nuclear matter.

If the effect of nuclear matter on the nucleon is similar to the effect of a potential with a small imaginary part, the nucleon must propagate like an attenuated plane wave. Suppose that the wave number is m, the frequency is $(T_m + V_m)/\hbar$, and the damping is $\Gamma_m/\hbar$. The Green's function is, accordingly,

$$S_m(t) = \exp\left[i(T_m + V_m - i\Gamma_m)t\right], \quad \text{for} \quad t<0, \quad (5.27)$$

and this has the Fourier transform

$$S_m^{(r)}(z) = (T_m + V_m - i\Gamma_m - z)^{-1}. \quad (5.28)$$

This cannot be exact, as the real Green's function is analytic everywhere except on the real axis, satisfies Eq. (5.17), and has a retarded part which is real on the real axis below $z = \mu(N)$. However, the imaginary part of this expression on the real axis yields a strength function, according to Eq. (5.21), and this is

$$g_m(x) = \Gamma_m/\pi\left[(T_m + V_m - x)^2 + \Gamma_m^2\right]. \quad (5.29)$$

This can be used in the dispersion relations to construct a Green's function which has all the correct properties. If Eq. (5.27) is valid for fairly large negative values of t, the real strength function must have the form of Eq. (5.29) in the neighbourhood of $x = T_m + V_m$. If the damping is small, the strength function is sharply peaked in this neighbourhood.

The calculations of the previous section show that the Green's function does indeed behave somewhat like this, if the results of the first two orders of perturbation theory are to be believed. The first term on the right of Eq. (5.26) gives a contribution only to V_k; it does not give any damping of the plane wave. The other two terms give real and imaginary contributions to $\Sigma_k(z)$ which are dependent on z. If the interaction is not very strong, the imaginary part is quite small, because it is a second order effect. It is particularly small if z is close to the Fermi energy, because the energy denominators in Eq. (5.26) vanish for very few combinations of l, m, and m' or l, l', and m in that case. We therefore expect the strength function to be large only if $T_k + \text{Re } \Sigma_k(x) - x$ is very close to zero. We define V_k as the value of Σ_k when this expression is zero, so that it satisfies

$$V_k = \text{Re } \Sigma_k(x_0), \quad x_0 = T_k + V_k. \quad (5.30)$$

In this neighbourhood, the strength function should be given approximately by Eq. (5.29), where the damping is

$$\Gamma_m = \text{Im } \Sigma_m(T_m + V_m), \quad (5.31)$$

so that the Green's function does behave as if there were a pole at $z = T_m + V_m - i\Gamma_m$. This pole is not in the upper half plane, and it must be reached by analytic continuation across the right-hand cut shown in Fig. 16. Γ_k is very small if k is close to the Fermi surface, and is, in fact, proportional to $(k - k_F)^2$ in this region, as was shown by Hugenholtz (1957). However, even for k close to the Fermi surface, $\Sigma_k(z)$ does depend on z, and this z-dependence reduces the residue of the pole at $z = T_k + V_k - i\Gamma_k$ to something less than unity (Thouless, 1959). This means that a particle with momentum close to the Fermi momentum has an energy distribution which is strongly peaked near $\mu(N)$, the energy obtained by adding one particle to the system in equilibrium, but the distribution has a high-energy tail.

We can use this model of nuclear matter to describe the scattering of a nucleon by an actual nucleus. The nucleon comes in from outside with positive energy, passes through a surface region of varying nuclear density, and reaches the central region of constant density still with the same energy. Since the relation between energy and momentum is different in free space and in nuclear matter, because of the potential energy V_k defined by Eq. (5.30), the momentum must increase as the nucleon penetrates the surface of the nucleus. Some comparisons have been made between the calculations of the potential energy of a particle in nuclear matter by Brueckner and Gammel (1958a) and the analysis of neutron and proton scattering data, but the comparisons have not been detailed. The potential energy should include the rearrangement energy defined by Eq. (4.48), which has been calculated by Brueckner et al. (1960a). Calculations of the imaginary part of the potential along these lines have been carried out by Shaw (1959). The most important conclusion to be drawn from this work is that most of the absorption should occur in the surface, because there are more states with the same energy as the initial state where the density is lower.

This model of the scattering of a nucleon by a nucleus is not reliable, because it does not take proper account of the variation of nuclear density in the surface of the nucleus. It is possible to go through a similar argument using shell-model wave functions instead of plane waves as the basis of the representation. If one nucleon in a particular shell-model state is added to the ground state of a nucleus, the state obtained is a mixture of eigenstates of the Hamiltonian, and the distribution of eigenvalues is given by the strength function. If the strength function is strongly peaked at a certain value, the optical model is a good approximation, and the width of the peak is related to the imaginary part of the potential. A full discussion of this approach to the optical model has been given by Brown (1959).

5. The Fermi liquid

There are only two substances which appear to be liquids at the absolute zero of temperature, and these are the two isotopes of helium,

He³ and He⁴. The fact that they are liquids must be a quantum mechanical effect, since only the zero-point motion of the atoms can prevent them from forming a solid. There is a striking difference between the two isotopes, since the naturally occurring He⁴ becomes superfluid at a temperature 2.2°, while He³ behaves as a normal fluid down to 0.1°. The superfluidity of He⁴ appears to be due to the fact that the atoms are bosons, as we discuss in Chapter IX. The atoms of He³ are fermions with spin one half, and it is expected that the antisymmetry of the wave function for liquid He³ should be as important as the symmetry of the wave function is for liquid He⁴.

The theory of the Fermi liquid was developed by Landau (1956) to serve as a theoretical description of liquid He³. The basic assumption is that the excitation spectrum of the system of interacting fermions has the same form as the excitation spectrum of noninteracting fermions. The simplest way of exciting a system of noninteracting fermions in its ground state is to remove one particle from below the Fermi surface and put it in a level above the Fermi surface, or, in other words, to create one particle and one hole. The assumption of the Fermi liquid theory is that as an interaction between the particles is switched on, the form of the excitation spectrum is unchanged. The simple excitations are still described as the addition of one particle to a level, or the removal of one particle from a level. As a result of the interaction, the rest of the medium must affect the added (or removed) particle, so that the excited state wave function is not simply a product of the ground state wave function with a single-particle wave function, but includes correlation between the extra (or missing) particle and the medium. For this reason, the excitation is referred to as the addition (or removal) of a *quasiparticle*. The quasiparticle has definite spin and momentum, and only one quasiparticle can be put into each level. All quasiparticle levels are filled up to the Fermi momentum, which is assumed to be unchanged by the interaction, so that the total number of quasiparticles is equal to the total number of particles. The quasiparticle excitation is unstable, and decays after a certain length of time.

These assumptions are very similar to the assumptions of the optical model that we discussed in the previous section. The quasiparticles correspond to the single particles of the optical model, and the assumption is that the Green's function has the form

$$S_m(t) = \exp\{i[\epsilon(m) - i\Gamma(m)]t\}, \quad \text{for} \quad t < 0, \quad (5.32)$$

for states above the Fermi surface, and is

$$S_l(t) = -\exp\{i[\epsilon(l) + i\Gamma(l)]t\}, \quad \text{for} \quad t \geq 0, \quad (5.33)$$

for states below the Fermi surface. We have shown that this assumption is partially justified by perturbation theory.

It should be noticed that as the true ground state corresponds to the physical vacuum in field theory, a quasiparticle state corresponds to a physical particle in field theory. Its propagator is given in perturbation theory by the sum of all linked graphs with an external line. The simple physical particle in a Fermi liquid corresponds to a bare particle in field theory.

The energy of a quasiparticle is defined in terms of the variation of the total energy per unit volume of the system as the density of quasiparticles is varied,

$$\delta E = (8\pi^3)^{-1} \sum_\sigma \int \epsilon(k)\,\delta n(\mathbf{k},\,\sigma)\,d^3k. \qquad (5.34)$$

Here $\delta n(\mathbf{k},\,\sigma)$ is the change in the density of quasiparticles with a particular momentum and spin. The quasiparticle energy is a smooth function of momentum, which behaves near the Fermi surface like

$$\epsilon(k) = \mu + \hbar^2(k^2 - k_F^2)/2M^*. \qquad (5.35)$$

The quantity μ is the chemical potential, since $\epsilon(k_F)$ is the energy needed to add one particle without altering the equilibrium, and M^* is known as the effective mass.

The entropy of a state with a particular distribution of quasiparticles is

$$S = -(8\pi^3)^{-1} \sum_\sigma \int \{n(\mathbf{k},\,\sigma)\,\log n(\mathbf{k},\,\sigma)$$
$$+ [1 - n(\mathbf{k},\,\sigma)]\,\log[1 - n(\mathbf{k},\,\sigma)]\}d^3k. \qquad (5.36)$$

This has the same form as it has for noninteracting particles, since the entropy depends just on the statistical weight of a distribution, and this does not depend on whether we are referring to particles or quasiparticles. From these formulas, thermodynamic properties at very low temperatures can be calculated. The specific heat is proportional to the temperature, and the constant of proportionality involves only the effective mass and the density. According to the measurements of Brewer and associates (1959), the low temperature specific heat shows that the effective mass is very close to twice the mass of an atom of He^3.

The other function which comes into the theory is essentially the second derivative of the total energy with respect to the occupation number of the states. From Eq. (5.34), we can see that the value of

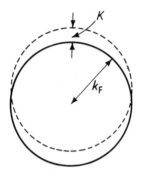

FIG. 20. A small displacement of the Fermi surface.

$\epsilon(k, \sigma)$ away from equilibrium is related to its value ϵ_0 at equilibrium by

$$\epsilon(\mathbf{k}, \sigma) = \epsilon_0(k) + (2\pi)^{-3} \sum_{\sigma'} \int f(\mathbf{k}, \sigma; \mathbf{k'}, \sigma') \delta n(\mathbf{k'}, \sigma') d^3k', \qquad (5.37)$$

where $f(\mathbf{k}, \sigma; \mathbf{k'}, \sigma')$ is this second derivative. It must, of course, satisfy

$$f(\mathbf{k}, \sigma; \mathbf{k'}, \sigma') = f(\mathbf{k'}, \sigma'; \mathbf{k}, \sigma). \qquad (5.38)$$

All higher derivatives are neglected in this theory.

There is an important sum rule which relates this function to the effective mass. Suppose that we displace the Fermi surface by a small amount $\mathbf{K}$, without changing its size or shape, as is shown in Fig. 20. This has the effect of giving the whole fluid a velocity $\hbar\mathbf{K}/M$, and so must increase the energy by $\rho\hbar^2K^2/2M$, where ρ is the total density of particles, since this is the kinetic energy added. Because the relative motion of the particles is unchanged, there can be no change of potential energy. This energy change can also be found from Eqs. (5.34) and (5.37), so that we have

$$\rho\hbar^2K^2/2M = (2\pi)^{-3} \sum_{\sigma} \int \epsilon_0(k) \delta n(\mathbf{k}, \sigma) d^3k$$

$$+ \tfrac{1}{2}(2\pi)^{-6} \sum_{\sigma} \sum_{\sigma'} \iint \delta n(\mathbf{k}, \sigma) f(\mathbf{k}, \sigma, \mathbf{k'}, \sigma') \delta n(\mathbf{k'}, \sigma') d^3k d^3k'. \qquad (5.39)$$

According to Fig. 20, $\delta n(k, \sigma)$ is equal to ± 1 in a region of momentum space very close to the Fermi surface with thickness $K \cos \theta$. The first term of Eq. (5.39) gives $\rho\hbar^2K^2/2M^*$. In the second term only values of k very close to k_F are involved, and it is reasonable to neglect the dependence of f on the magnitudes of $\mathbf{k}$ and $\mathbf{k'}$ in this region. The equation yields

$$1/M = 1/M^* + (k_F/8\pi^2\hbar^2) \sum_{\sigma} \sum_{\sigma'} \int_{-1}^{1} f_{\sigma\sigma'}(\cos \theta) \cos\theta \, d(\cos \theta). \qquad (5.40)$$

We have written $f_{\sigma\sigma'}(\cos \theta)$ for the value of $f(\mathbf{k}, \sigma; \mathbf{k'}, \sigma')$ with $\mathbf{k}$ and $\mathbf{k'}$ both on the Fermi surface, where θ is the angle between $\mathbf{k}$ and $\mathbf{k'}$.

Various other physical properties are simply related to the function $f_{\sigma\sigma'}$ (cos θ), and many of these are discussed in the review article by Abrikosov and Khalatnikov (1959). For example, the magnetic susceptibility at low temperatures is determined by the spin-dependence of this function. Other properties, such as viscosity and thermal conductivity, are affected by the lifetimes of the quasiparticles. From the arguments sketched in the previous section, we expect the lifetime of a quasiparticle at zero temperature to be inversely proportional to the square of its distance from the Fermi surface. A quasiparticle close to the Fermi surface has a lifetime proportional to T^{-2} at a temperature T, because the width of the region in momentum space round the Fermi surface in which levels are partially occupied is proportional to T. Experimental measurements of the properties of liquid He³ which depend on the lifetime do not agree very well with the theory.

6. Sound and zero sound

One of the most interesting predictions of the Fermi liquid theory is concerned with the propagation of sound at very low temperatures. Imagine that a large volume of the liquid is divided up into small cells which are large enough to contain very many atoms. We can describe the distribution of quasiparticles in each of these cells. We suppose that there is some periodic disturbance in the medium, so that the distribution varies gradually from one cell to the next. If the period of the disturbance is much longer than the lifetime of the quasiparticles, there will be equilibrium within each cell, and everything can be described by a local velocity and density. In this case, sound waves propagate in the usual way, with a velocity c which depends on the compressibility. We can use the relation

$$c^2 = \frac{1}{M}\frac{\partial p}{\partial \rho} = \frac{\partial p}{\partial \mu}\frac{1}{M}\frac{\partial \mu}{\partial \rho} = \frac{\rho}{M}\frac{\partial \mu}{\partial \rho}, \tag{5.41}$$

where μ is the chemical potential, equal to $\epsilon(k_F)$. If the density of particles is increased, the Fermi surface expands, remaining spherical, so that we have

$$\rho = k_F{}^3/3\pi^2,$$

$$\delta\rho = k_F{}^2\delta k_F/\pi^2. \tag{5.42}$$

We can calculate the change in μ using Eqs. (5.35) and (5.37), and we get

$$\delta\mu = \frac{d\epsilon_0(k)}{dk}\delta k_F + (2\pi)^{-3}\sum_{\sigma'}\int f(k_F, \sigma; k', \sigma')\,\delta n(k', \sigma')d^3k$$

$$= \hbar^2 k_F\delta k_F/M^* + (2\pi)^{-2}k_F{}^2\delta k_F\sum_{\sigma'}\int_{-1}^{1}f_{\sigma\sigma'}(\cos\theta)d(\cos\theta). \tag{5.43}$$

Substituting Eqs. (5.42) and (5.43) in Eq. (5.41) and using the value of M^* given by Eq. (5.40), we get

$$c^2 = (k_F{}^2/3M^2)(1 + F_0)/(1 + \tfrac{1}{3}F_1), \qquad (5.44)$$

where the spin average of $f_{\sigma\sigma'}(\cos\theta)$ has been expanded as a series of Legendre polynomials

$$\tfrac{1}{2}\sum_{\sigma'} k_F M^* f_{\sigma\sigma'}(\cos\theta)/\pi^2\hbar^2 = \sum_n F_n P_n(\cos\theta). \qquad (5.45)$$

Since the low-temperature specific heat determines F_1, a measurement of the sound velocity at low temperatures determines F_0. The measurements of Laquer and co-workers (1959) give the velocity as 183 metres/sec at low temperatures, and this gives $F_0 = 7.6$, if F_1 is 3.0.

If the frequency is raised or the temperature is lowered, the lifetime of the quasiparticles must eventually become comparable with the frequency, and there will not be time for equilibrium to be established. The sound waves are therefore damped out under such conditions. At very high frequencies, disturbances can be propagated, but these are not like sound waves, since there is no local equilibrium. If the particles did not interact at all, any disturbance would propagate with velocity k_F/M, since this is the velocity of those particles which are free to move; this must be compared with the limit of the sound velocity as the interaction goes to zero, which is $k_F/\sqrt{3}M$, as can be seen by putting $F_0 = F_1 = 0$ in Eq. (5.44). The disturbance which propagates at very low temperatures or very high frequencies is called *zero sound*.

We can derive the velocity of zero sound by using the kinetic equation

$$\frac{\partial n}{\partial t} + \frac{1}{\hbar}\frac{\partial n}{\partial \mathbf{r}}\cdot\frac{\partial \epsilon}{\partial \mathbf{k}} - \frac{1}{\hbar}\frac{\partial n}{\partial \mathbf{k}}\cdot\frac{\partial \epsilon}{\partial \mathbf{r}} = I(n). \qquad (5.46)$$

The first term on the left gives the change in the distribution of quasiparticles within a cell, the second gives the change due to the movement of quasiparticles from one cell to another with velocity $\partial\epsilon/\partial\mathbf{k}$, and the third gives the change in momentum of a quasiparticle due to the potential gradient acting on it. The right hand side gives the change due to collisions, which we ignore, since we are assuming that the lifetime of the quasiparticles is long. We are looking for a periodic solution of this equation, so we try a solution of the form

$$n(\mathbf{k}, \sigma) = n_0(\mathbf{k}, \sigma) + \delta n(\mathbf{k}, \sigma)\exp[i(\mathbf{q}\cdot\mathbf{r} - \omega t)]. \qquad (5.47)$$

If we keep only terms of first order in δn in Eq. (5.46), we get

$$\left(-\omega + \frac{1}{\hbar}\mathbf{q}\cdot\frac{\partial\epsilon}{\partial\mathbf{k}}\right)\delta n(\mathbf{k},\,\sigma)$$

$$-\frac{1}{\hbar}\frac{\partial n_0}{\partial\epsilon}\frac{\partial\epsilon}{\partial\mathbf{k}}\cdot\mathbf{q}(2\pi)^{-3}\sum_{\sigma'}\int f(\mathbf{k},\,\sigma;\,\mathbf{k}',\,\sigma')\,\delta n(\mathbf{k}',\,\sigma')\,d^3k' = 0. \quad (5.48)$$

We can solve this equation by putting

$$\delta n(\mathbf{k},\,\sigma) = (\partial n_0/\partial\epsilon)\nu_\sigma(\theta,\,\varphi), \quad (5.49)$$

where θ and φ are the polar angles of $\mathbf{k}$ measured from the direction of $\mathbf{q}$. At low temperatures, $\partial n_0/\partial\epsilon$ is nearly equal to minus a δ-function, and the magnitude of $\partial\epsilon/\partial\mathbf{k}$ is $\hbar v_F = \hbar^2 k_F/M^*$ wherever $\partial n_0/\partial\epsilon$ is not negligible. Writing u for the velocity ω/q of the disturbance, we get

$$(u - v_F\cos\theta)\nu_\sigma(\theta,\,\varphi) = (2\pi)^{-3}k_F{}^2\cos\theta\sum_{\sigma'}\int f_{\sigma\sigma'}(\cos\chi)\nu_\sigma(\theta',\,\varphi')\,d\Omega',$$

$$(5.50)$$

where χ is the angle between $(\theta,\,\varphi)$ and $(\theta',\,\varphi')$.

In the simple case $f_{\sigma\sigma'}(\cos\theta) = \pi^2\hbar^2 F_0/M^* k_F$, Eq. (5.50) shows that $\nu_\sigma(\theta,\,\varphi)$ is proportional to $v_F\cos\theta/(u - v_F\cos\theta)$. Substitution of this into the right hand side of Eq. (5.50) gives an equation for $s = u/v_F$,

$$\cos\theta = \tfrac{1}{2}F_0\cos\theta\int_{-1}^{1}\cos\theta(s-\cos\theta)^{-1}\,d(\cos\theta),$$

$$F_0{}^{-1} = \tfrac{1}{2}s\log\left[(s+1)/(s-1)\right]^{-1}. \quad (5.51)$$

For free particles, this equation gives $s = 1$, so u is equal to v_F, which is $\sqrt{3}$ times the sound velocity. There is always a solution for positive F_0, and, for F_0 large, the solution tends to $u = v_F\sqrt{F_0/3}$, which agrees with the sound velocity given by Eq. (5.44).

With a more complicated form of f, Eq. (5.50) becomes more complicated, and can have a number of different types of solution. If the solution $\nu_\sigma(\theta,\,\varphi)$ does not depend on spin, the disturbance is called zero sound, and if it does depend on spin, the disturbance is a spin wave. Abrikosov and Khalatnikov (1959) have studied this equation, and they came to the conclusion that spin waves probably should not exist in He³, but zero sound should exist. They estimate that the frequency needed to observe zero sound is greater than 10^{10} cycles per second at 0.1°.

The observation of zero sound would be a satisfying confirmation of Landau's theory of the Fermi liquid. It is difficult to devise any other conclusive test of the theory, since the number of free parameters is rather greater than the number of quantities which can be measured for He^3 at very low temperatures.

7. Collective motion

We have discussed sound and zero sound in a Fermi liquid in some detail because they are examples of two different types of collective motion. Our descriptions have been macroscopic, since we have considered how the distribution of quasiparticles varies in space, but we have not considered what happens to the individual quasiparticles. We know that the collective motion must be quantized, and it is not hard to guess what form a quantized theory should have. Since sound and zero sound are forms of vibration, we expect that each mode of vibration should be quantized like a harmonic oscillator. The quanta, or phonons, of a sound wave with velocity c and wavenumber q have energy $\hbar c q$, and each mode contributes a zero-point energy $\frac{1}{2}\hbar c q$ to the energy of the ground state of the liquid. We show later that a single phonon of zero sound consists, to a first approximation, of a coherent superposition of states which can be obtained by giving extra momentum $\hbar q$ to one of the quasiparticles in the equilibrium state. Ordinary sound in a Fermi liquid cannot be so readily described in terms of the excitation of quasiparticles, since it depends for its existence on the comparatively short lifetime of the quasiparticles.

There are many other types of collective motion which are of interest in the theory of many-fermion systems. The simplest type of motion is the motion of the centre of mass, with the relative motion unchanged. Invariance arguments give all the information we need about this, and it is clear that a free system with mass NM increases its energy by $\hbar^2 K^2 / 2NM$ when the momentum of its centre of mass changes from zero to $\hbar K$ without any change of the motion of the particles relative to the centre of mass. Although this is an obvious result, it serves to check the validity of any theory of collective motion; a method which gives the wrong answer when applied to this problem cannot be trusted when it is applied to some other problem.

More interesting types of collective motion than this are encountered in nuclear physics. The existence of a collective mode is usually deduced from "macroscopic" considerations, in the sense that the nucleus is considered as a liquid drop. Although nuclear matter is not easily compressible, so that the energy of a mode involving compression of the nucleus would be very high, the surface of a liquid drop can vibrate about its equilibrium position without compressing the liquid. The angular dependence of the amplitude of the vibration can be expressed as a sum of spherical harmonics, and, for small vibrations about a spherical equilibrium shape, the different harmonics are not coupled. Each spherical harmonic corresponds to a different mode of vibration, and again the method of quantization is obvious. The order of the spherical harmonic gives the angular momentum (measured in units of $\hbar$) of the first excited state of the quantized vibrating system. The zero order harmonic (breathing mode) does not generally occur, because this represents a change in the volume of the drop. The first order harmonic (dipole) represents a simple displacement of the drop, so this is not a real vibration, but all higher orders may occur. The vibrational states that are of most interest in nuclei are quadrupole (second order harmonic) and octupole (third order harmonic) vibrations. These were originally discussed by Bohr and Mottelson (1953).

Another type of collective motion occurs in nonspherical nuclei. A spherical nucleus cannot rotate, since rotation would not alter its wave function, but a spheroidal nucleus can rotate about an axis perpendicular to its axis of symmetry. When the rotation of an axially symmetric body is quantized, the energy levels become

$$E - E_0 = \hbar^2 J(J + 1)/2\mathscr{I}, \qquad (5.52)$$

where J is the angular momentum, and $\mathscr{I}$ is the moment of inertia.[†] Because the nucleus is symmetrical about its centre, J must be even. These levels were shown to exist in nuclei by Bohr and Mottelson (1953).

A third type of collective motion was suggested by Goldhaber and Teller (1948). In this type of motion, the protons do not move relative to one another, nor do the neutrons, but the protons and neutrons vibrate against one another. The frequency of this vibration is very great, so that only the first excited state of the collective motion is of any interest. This dipole state should be strongly excited from the ground state by electromagnetic radiation, and accounts for the "giant dipole resonance", the strongly peaked absorption of photons of quite high energies observed in medium and heavy nuclei.

The formal quantum mechanical treatment of collective motion is based on such simple physical pictures of the motion. A very convenient quantum theory of collective motion was proposed by Tomonaga (1955a). We start with $3N$ coordinates and $3N$ momenta as variables describing the N particles. In the case of centre of mass motion, it is possible to transform to a new system of variables which includes the total momentum and the coordinates of the centre of mass as separate variables. These three momenta and three coordinates are the *collective*

[†] L. Landau and E. Lifshitz, "Quantum Mechanics," pp. 373–376, Addison-Wesley, Reading, Massachusetts, 1958.

variables, while the remaining $3N-3$ momenta and coordinates are called *internal variables*. This new system of variables should satisfy the same commutation relations as the old one. We know that if the internal variables are orthogonal to the collective variables, the Hamiltonian does separate into two parts, one containing only the centre of mass (collective) variables, and one containing the internal variables.

The situation is more complicated for other types of collective motion, since there is no reason to believe that the Hamiltonian does separate completely into a collective part and an internal part. We deduce the existence of these other types of collective motion, not from an invariance principle, but from a simplified physical picture of the system. The method proposed by Tomonaga is to guess a collective momentum π corresponding to the collective mode we are examining. In the example he gives of the quadrupole oscillation of a cirular two-dimensional drop, π is given by

$$\pi = -i\hbar \sum_{n=1}^{N} (x_n \partial/\partial x_n - y_n \partial/\partial y_n). \qquad (5.53)$$

This momentum must commute with all the internal coordinates, and the collective coordinate ξ has to be orthogonal to all the internal coordinates. A suitable collective coordinate is

$$\xi = (NR_0^2)^{-1} \sum_{n=1}^{N} (x_n^2 - y_n^2), \qquad (5.54)$$

where R_0 is a constant. The commutation relation between π and ξ is

$$[\pi, \xi] = -i\hbar (NR_0^2)^{-1} 2 \sum_{n} (x_n^2 + y_n^2). \qquad (5.55)$$

If π and ξ were truly canonical variables, the commutator would be $-i\hbar$. The argument is that since there are a large number of particles in the system, $\sum_n (x_n^2 + y_n^2)$ only deviates from its mean value by a small amount, and, if R_0^2 is equal to twice the average value of $(x_n^2 + y_n^2)$, the canonical commutation relation is very nearly obtained.

It is not surprising that the separation of a collective mode should require the physical assumption that some expression does not deviate much from its mean value. In the transition from a microscopic classical theory to a macroscopic theory, a similar assumption always has to be made.

The next step is to separate those parts of the Hamiltonian which involve the collective variables from the rest of the Hamiltonian. The collective momentum will occur in the form $\pi^2/2I$, where I is some *mass parameter*. If this is subtracted from the kinetic energy, the remainder should not contain π, and so should commute with the collective co-ordinate ξ. Since we have, from Eqs. (5.54), (5.55), and (5.53),

$$-(\hbar^2/2M) \sum_n [\partial^2/\partial x_n^2 + \partial^2/\partial y_n^2, \xi]$$

$$= -(2\hbar^2/MNR_0^2) \sum_n (x_n \partial/\partial x_n - y_n \partial/\partial y_n),$$

$$[\pi^2, \xi] = -2i\hbar\pi = -2\sum_n \hbar^2 (x_n \partial/\partial x_n - y_n \partial/\partial y_n), \qquad (5.56)$$

the mass parameter is

$$I = \tfrac{1}{2} MNR_0^2. \qquad (5.57)$$

The coordinate ξ is separated from the Hamiltonian in a similar way. Since $[\pi, \xi] = -i\hbar$ is only approximately satisfied, ξ occurs in the kinetic energy as well as in the potential energy. The Hamiltonian can be expanded in powers of ξ, so that the leading terms in the expansion are

$$H = (T_0 + V_0) + \xi(T_1 + V_1) + \xi^2(T_2 + V_2) + \pi^2/2I + \cdots, \qquad (5.58)$$

where all the coefficients are functions of the internal coordinates and momenta. The term independent of the collective variables gives the internal motion, the term quadratic in the collective variables gives the collective oscillation, and the linear term gives a coupling between the two, which should be small for the theory to be satisfactory.

The collective variable method can be used for almost any kind of physical system. The average value which occurs, for example, in Eq. (5.55) depends on the system and on the conditions which are imposed on it, but the method used for separation of the collective variable is quite general. The collective variable is usually symmetric under interchange of the particles, and so all the effects of the antisymmetry of the wave function must go into that part of the wave function which depends on the internal variables. The internal variables are very complicated, since they are orthogonal to the collective variables, and it is very difficult to handle them, as we observed in Chapter II. For this reason, it is sometimes more convenient to leave all the original particle coordinates and momenta as internal variables, and to introduce collective variables in addition, using more variables than there are degrees of freedom in the system. The redundant variables are later removed by subsidiary conditions which relate the internal variables to the collective variables. This method is used by Elliott and Skyrme (1955) in their discussion of how to correct the nuclear shell model for the spurious centre of mass motion which it introduces.

Another difficulty with this method is that it provides no way of determining the nature of the collective motion from the form of the

Hamiltonian. We have to guess the appropriate collective variables, and then see if the Hamiltonian separates into a collective and an internal part. This difficulty is particularly clear in the case of rotational motion of the nucleus. The appropriate collective momentum is the angular momentum, but the mass parameter, in this case the moment of inertia, depends on the collective coordinate chosen. If the coordinate is a good one, the Hamiltonian should be almost independent of the coordinate, since the Hamiltonian for a rotating body is a function which is independent of the orientation of the body. Two extreme assumptions for a nucleus are that it rotates like an irrotational fluid, or like a rigid body. In either case the moment of inertia is easy to calculate, but there is no evidence that the Hamiltonian does in fact separate in either manner. This problem has been discussed in these terms by Bohr and Mottelson (1958). The observed moments of inertia appear to lie between the two, closer to the rigid body value.

8. Generator coordinates

This method of studying collective motion in nuclei (or other many-fermion systems) was proposed by Hill and Wheeler (1953). It is less general method than the collective variables method of Tomonaga, since it is based on the observation that the shell model gives a good description of nuclei. A shell model potential is used which depends on some parameter α, the *generator coordinate*. For example, in the case of rotational motion studied by Peierls and Yoccoz (1957), the parameter is the orientation of the axis of the spheroidal potential. If the potential is a self-consistent potential, the determinant of the lowest shell-model wave functions should minimize the expectation value of the Hamiltonian, but this expectation value does not depend on the orientation of the potential. In the simplest form of the theory (Peierls and Yoccoz, 1957; Griffin and Wheeler, 1957), a new wave function Ψ, which is a linear combination of the shell model wave functions Φ_α for different values of α, is used to evaluate the expectation value of the Hamiltonian. The new wave function is

$$\Psi = \int f(\alpha)\,\Phi_\alpha\,d\alpha, \qquad (5.59)$$

and the condition that the expectation value of the Hamiltonian should be stationary gives a homogeneous linear equation for $f(\alpha)$. The solution with the lowest eigenvalue gives a better approximation for the ground state than Φ_α, and the other solutions give wave functions for collective excited states. In the rotational case, $f(\alpha)$ must be a spherical harmonic, and all that is necessary to calculate the energies of rotational levels is to calculate the expectation value of the Hamiltonian; such calculations have been performed by Yoccoz (1957).

The weakness of this method is shown up by the fact that it does not yield the correct dependence of the energy of a nucleus on its linear momentum, which we know from invariance considerations; this was demonstrated in the paper of Peierls and Yoccoz (1957). A method of overcoming this difficulty has been proposed by Gross (1960b). The shell model wave function is multiplied by an exponential of a multiple of the collective coordinate chosen to give the shell model wave function a particular average value of the collective momentum. A linear combination of these products is then used as a trial wave function. In the case of translational motion, the ground state is found in the same way as in the simpler theory, but the energy of a state of momentum P is found by giving the shell model potential a velocity P/NM before selecting the component with momentum P. For the rotational problem, only the first of these two steps is carried out; the wave function is given an angular velocity, but no eigenfunction of angular momentum is projected out. Gross shows that this method gives the "cranking model" formula for the moment of inertia. The cranking model formula was originally derived by Inglis (1954, 1956), who assumed that the nucleons move in a spheroidal potential which is driven slowly round with angular velocity ω. The dependence of the energy on ω gives the moment of inertia. The cranking model is found to be in very good agreement with experiment, when corrections for "pairing effects" are made (Griffin and Rich, 1960).

9. Two-particle Green's functions

In the earlier part of this chapter we studied the one-particle Green's functions defined by Eq. (5.1), and found that they gave information about those states which can be obtained by adding one particle to or removing one particle from the ground state of a system of N particles. From a knowledge of the one-particle Green's function it is possible to calculate the expectation value of a one-particle operator, but it is not generally possible to calculate the expectation value of a two-particle operator, except for the potential energy operator. The one-particle Green's function gives information about the excited states of the $N + 1$ and $N - 1$ particle systems, but it gives no information about the excited states of the N-particle system. For these reasons, it is important to know also the two-particle Green's functions, which are defined by

$$G(k_1, t_1; k_2, t_2; k_3, t_3; k_4, t_4)$$
$$= \langle \Psi_0 | T[a_{k_1}{}^\dagger(t_1) a_{k_2}(t_2) a_{k_3}{}^\dagger(t_3) a_{k_4}(t_4)] | \Psi_0 \rangle. \qquad (5.60)$$

This definition is a generalization of Eq. (5.1). There are some obvious symmetry relations which this function satisfies. When two of the time variables coincide there may be a discontinuity, and the magnitude of this discontinuity is equal to a one-particle Green's function. Various dispersion relations can be constructed, but the function is so complicated in this general form that we shall not attempt to study it, but consider only some special cases.

The right hand side of Eq. (5.60) can be expanded as a sum of products of matrix elements of the creation and annihilation operators between eigenstates of the Hamiltonian. Three intermediate states occur in each term of the sum. The first and third intermediate states are those states of the $N \pm 1$ particle systems which determine the properties of the one-particle Green's function. The second intermediate state contains $N + 2$ particles if t_1 and t_3 are both less than t_2 and t_4, it contains $N - 2$ particles if t_2 and t_4 are both less than t_1 and t_3, and it contains N particles otherwise. Since we know something about the first and third intermediate states from the one-particle Green's functions, it is the second intermediate state in which we are most interested. We can suppress the dependence of the two-particle Green's functions on the $N \pm 1$ particle states by pairing off the time variables, and making the members of a pair equal. The two ways of pairing the variables give rise to two functions of one variable, which we denote by

$$G(k_2, k_1; k_3, k_4; t_1 - t_2) = G(k_1, t_2; k_2, t_2; k_3, t_1; k_4, t_1)$$

$$= \begin{cases} \langle \Psi_0 | a_{k_1}{}^\dagger a_{k_2} \exp[i(H - E_0)(t_1 - t_2)] a_{k_3}{}^\dagger a_{k_4} | \Psi_0 \rangle, & \text{for } t_1 < t_2, \\ & \qquad (5.61) \\ \langle \Psi_0 | a_{k_3}{}^\dagger a_{k_4} \exp[-i(H - E_0)(t_1 - t_2)] a_{k_1}{}^\dagger a_{k_2} | \Psi_0 \rangle, & \text{for } t_1 > t_2, \end{cases}$$

and

$$\mathcal{G}(k_1, k_3; k_2, k_4; t_1 - t_2) = G(k_1, t_2; k_2, t_1; k_3, t_2; k_4, t_1)$$

$$= \begin{cases} \langle \Psi_0 | a_{k_3}{}^\dagger a_{k_1}{}^\dagger \exp[i(H - E_0)(t_1 - t_2)] a_{k_2} a_{k_4} | \Psi_0 \rangle, & \text{for } t_1 \leq t_2, \\ & \qquad (5.62) \\ \langle \Psi_0 | a_{k_2} a_{k_4} \exp[-i(H - E_0)(t_1 - t_2)] a_{k_3}{}^\dagger a_{k_1}{}^\dagger | \Psi_0 \rangle, & \text{for } t_1 > t_2. \end{cases}$$

The second of these functions plays an important role in the theory of superconductivity, and we give a brief discussion of it in Chapter VIII, Sec. 8, but the Green's function defined by Eq. (5.61) is particularly useful. Since it depends on only one time variable, we can take the Fourier transforms of the advanced and retarded parts using Eqs. (5.13) and (5.14). The Fourier transform of the retarded part of Eq. (5.61) is

$$G^{(r)}(k_2, k_1; k_3, k_4; z)$$

$$= \sum_n \langle \Psi_0 | a_{k_1}{}^\dagger a_{k_2} | \Psi_n \rangle (E_n - E_0 - z)^{-1} \langle \Psi_n | a_{k_3}{}^\dagger a_{k_4} | \Psi_0 \rangle. \quad (5.63)$$

An expression like this occurs if we calculate the response of a system to an external perturbation, using second order perturbation theory. For example, if we apply to nuclear matter an electrostatic potential periodic in space and time with amplitude B, wave number q, and frequency ω, the perturbing Hamiltonian is

$$\int e\rho^{(p)}(r) B \exp{(i\mathbf{q}\cdot\mathbf{r} - i\omega t)} d^3r = eB \exp{(-i\omega t)} \sum_k a_k^{(p)}{}^\dagger a_{k+q}^{(p)}$$

$$= eB \exp{(-i\omega t)} \rho_q^{(p)}. \quad (5.64)$$

We have written $\rho^{(p)}(r)$ for the density of protons at r, and $\rho_q^{(p)}$ for the qth Fourier component of this density operator. The forward scattering amplitude due to the nuclear matter is

$$eB^2 \sum_n \langle \Psi_0 | \rho_{-q}^{(p)} | \Psi_n \rangle (E_n - E_0 - \hbar\omega)^{-1} \langle \Psi_n | \rho_q^{(p)} | \Psi_0 \rangle$$

$$= eB^2 \sum_k^{(p)} \sum_{k'}^{(p)} G^{(r)}(k, k+q; k', k'+q; \hbar\omega), \quad (5.65)$$

where the sums on the right hand side are over proton operators only. This is the expression given by second order perturbation theory rewritten by use of Eq. (5.63).

The method we used for the calculation of the single-particle Green's functions from perturbation theory has been used for the calculation of two-particle Green's functions by Landau (1958). We have to add up all linked graphs with two external lines. We assume that, in principle, we know the one-particle Green's functions, and so we need only add up connected graphs (those with no fermion self-energy parts), using the true propagator $S_k(t)$ instead of the unperturbed propagator as the factor which a fermion line contributes. We can then calculate the two-particle Green's functions in terms of the sum $\Gamma(k_2, k_1; k_3, k_4; t)$ of all *irreducible vertex parts*. An irreducible vertex part is represented by a graph which has a vertex at time t where the line k_3 enters and the line k_4 leaves the graph, and a vertex at time zero where the line k_1 enters and the line k_2 leaves; it is irreducible if it is not possible to separate it

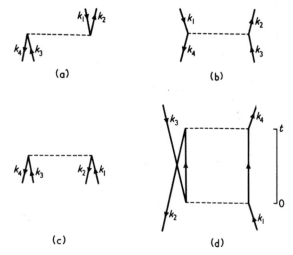

FIG. 21. Some irreducible vertex parts.

into two parts by breaking only two fermion lines at the same level. Some examples of irreducible vertex parts are shown in Fig. 21. In the same way as we derived Eq. (5.24), we get the equation

$$G(k_2, k_1; k_3, k_4; t) = S_{k_1}(0) S_{k_3}(0) \delta_{k_1 k_2} \delta_{k_3 k_4} - S_{k_1}(-t) S_{k_2}(t) \delta_{k_1 k_4} \delta_{k_2 k_3}$$

$$- \sum_{k_5} \sum_{k_6} \int_{-\infty}^{\infty} \int_{-\infty}^{\infty} S_{k_1}(-t') S_{k_2}(t') \Gamma(k_2, k_1; k_5, k_6; t'' - t')$$

$$\times [G(k_5, k_6; k_3, k_4; t - t'') - S_{k_5}(0) S_{k_3}(0) \delta_{k_5 k_6} \delta_{k_3 k_4}] \, dt' dt''. \qquad (5.66)$$

To use this equation, we make two simplifying assumptions. The first assumption is that the quasiparticle approximation is good, so that $S_k(t)$ can be replaced by an exponential as it is in Eqs. (5.32) and (5.33). This leads to

$$G(k_2, k_1; k_3, k_3; z] = [\theta_{k_1}(1 - \theta_{k_2}) - \theta_{k_2}(1 - \theta_{k_1})](\epsilon_{k_2} - \epsilon_{k_1} - z)^{-1}$$

$$\times [\delta_{k_1 k_4} \delta_{k_2 k_3} - \sum_{k_5} \sum_{k_6} \Gamma(k_2, k_1; k_5, k_6; z) G(k_5, k_6; k_3, k_4; z)], \qquad (5.67)$$

where we have neglected the damping of the quasiparticle states, and have written θ_k for the function which is unity for k inside the Fermi sea and zero for k outside the Fermi sea; ϵ_k is the quasiparticle energy.

We are particularly interested in the case in which the difference in momentum between k_1 and k_2, which must equal the difference in momentum between k_4 and k_3, is very small. In this limit it is reasonable to assume that $\Gamma(k, k + q; k', k' + q)$ is independent of q, unless the interaction has a long range, and has a singular behaviour for small momentum transfer. This reservation has to be made, since the first order contributions to Γ, shown in Figs. 21(a) and (c), behave like q^{-2} in the case of the Coulomb interaction. Equation (5.67) becomes

$$(\epsilon_k - \epsilon_{k+q} - z)G(k, k + q; k', k' + q; z)$$
$$= [\theta_{k+q}(1 - \theta_k) - \theta_k(1 - \theta_{k+q})]$$
$$\times[\delta_{kk'} - \sum_{k''}\Gamma(k, k; k'', k''; z)G(k'', k'' + q; k', k' + q; z)]. \quad (5.68)$$

The function $\Gamma(k, k; k'', k''; 0)$ can be identified with the $f(k, k'')$ which was introduced in Eq. (5.37) in the theory of a Fermi liquid, as has been shown by Landau (1958). The eigenvalues of the Hamiltonian are given by the poles of the Green's function, as is clear from Eq. (5.63), and the poles of the Green's function are given by the values of z for which the homogeneous part of Eq. (5.67) has a solution. The homogeneous part of Eq. (5.68) gives

$$(\epsilon_k - \epsilon_{k+q} - z_0)G(k, k + q; k', k' + q; z_0)$$
$$-[\theta_{k+q}(1 - \theta_k) - \theta_k(1 - \theta_{k+q})]$$
$$\times \sum_{k''}\Gamma(k, k; k'', k''; z_0)G(k'', k'' + q; k', k' + q; z_0) = 0. \quad (5.69)$$

We can identify this equation with Eq. (5.48), since Γ is equal to f, $\epsilon_{k+q} - \epsilon_k$ is equal to $\mathbf{q} \cdot \partial\epsilon/\partial\mathbf{k}$, and $[\theta_{k+q}(1 - \theta_k) - \theta_k(1 - \theta_{k+q})]$ is approximately equal to $\mathbf{q} \cdot \partial n_0/\partial\mathbf{k}$. This shows that a quantum of zero sound is a coherent excitation of one hole and one particle coupled together by the interactions.

The second simplifying assumption we can make is that only the first order contribution to the irreducible vertex part need be taken into account. These first order contributions are shown in Figs. 21(a), (b) and (c), and the approximation they give is

$$\Gamma(k_2, k_1; k_3, k_4; z) = V_{k_2 k_4, k_1 k_3} - V_{k_4 k_2, k_1 k_3}. \quad (5.70)$$

If q is the momentum difference between k_1 and k_2, and if the potential is local, so that its matrix elements are functions of momentum transfer only, this is $V(q) - V(|k_1 - k_4|)$, which goes to a finite limit as q goes to zero for a short-range force. Our second assumption therefore enables us to relate the function f which occurs in the Fermi liquid theory to the interaction between the particles. This approximation for f is equivalent to the Hartree-Fock approximation for the quasiparticle energies, and would yield the same value for the effective mass at the Fermi surface if substituted into Eq. (5.40). When these substitutions are made in Eq. (5.69), an equation linear in the strength of the interaction is obtained for the energies of the excited states of the system. This linearized equation gives an approximation which is often known as the *random phase approximation*.

10. Time-dependent Hartree-Fock theory

In Chapter VIII we discuss some other derivations of the random phase approximation which are all more or less easy to generalize. We discuss here a derivation which cannot be readily generalized, but which gives us a simple mechanical picture of what happens when a quantum system has collective motion. The method is semiclassical, so that a frequency rather than an energy comes out as the answer, and it is based on the Hartree-Fock approximation. This method has been discussed by a number of authors, including Zyrianov and Eleonskii (1956), Ferrell (1957), Goldstone and Gottfried (1959), and Ehrenreich and Cohen (1959).

The time-dependent Hartree-Fock equations were derived by Dirac (1930). The argument we give here is due to Frenkel (1934). The equations of motion in quantum mechanics can be derived from the condition that

$$\langle \delta\Psi(t) \,|\, (H - i\hbar\partial/\partial t) \,|\, \Psi(t) \rangle \tag{5.71}$$

should be stationary for small variations of the time-dependent state $|\Psi(t)\rangle$. If we impose on $|\Psi(t)\rangle$ the restriction that at any time is should be a single determinant, the time-dependent Hartree-Fock equations can be obtained in a straightforward manner. One solution of these equations is

$$|\Psi(t)\rangle = \exp(-iE_0 t/\hbar)\,|\Phi\rangle, \tag{5.72}$$

where $|\Phi\rangle$ satisfies the time-independent Hartree-Fock equations, which we discussed in Sec. 1 of Chapter III, and E_0 is the expectation value of the Hamiltonian, given by Eq. (3.8) in the representation which diagonalizes the self-consistent Hamiltonian (3.6). We look for solutions of the variational problem which represent small departures from this stationary solution.

We can use the representation of a determinantal wave function given by Eq. (3.29), and so we look for a solution of the form

$$|\Psi(t)\rangle = f(t)\,\exp\,(-iE_0 t/\hbar)\,\exp\,(\sum_{i=1}^{N}\sum_{m=N+1}^{\infty} C_{mi}(t)a_m{}^\dagger a_i)\,|\Phi\rangle, \tag{5.73}$$

where $f(t)$ and $C_{mi}(t)$ are arbitrary complex numbers. We use Eq. (3.30) to evaluate the expression (5.71) up to second order in the numbers

C_{mi}. To this order, the variational principle is satisfied if we have

$$(\epsilon_m - \epsilon_i) C_{mi}(t)$$

$$+ \sum_{j=1}^{N} \sum_{n=N+1}^{\infty} [(V_{mj,in} - V_{mj,ni}) C_{nj}(t) + (V_{mn,ij} - V_{mn,ji}) C_{nj}{}^*(t)]$$

$$= i\hbar dC_{mi}(t)/dt. \quad (5.74)$$

This equation has solutions of the form

$$C_{mi}(t) = X_{mi} \exp(-i\omega t) + Y_{mi}{}^* \exp(i\omega^* t) \quad (5.75)$$

if X_{mi} and Y_{mi} satisfy the equations

$$(\epsilon_m - \epsilon_i) X_{mi} + \sum_{j=1}^{N} \sum_{n=N+1}^{\infty} [(V_{mj,in} - V_{mj,ni}) X_{nj}$$

$$+ (V_{mn,ij} - V_{mn,ji}) Y_{nj}] = \hbar\omega X_{mi},$$

$$(\epsilon_m - \epsilon_i) Y_{mi} + \sum_{j=1}^{N} \sum_{n=N+1}^{\infty} [(V_{ij,mn} - V_{ij,nm}) X_{nj}$$

$$+ (V_{in,mj} - V_{in,jm}) Y_{nj}] = -\hbar\omega Y_{mi}. \quad (5.76)$$

This equation is the general equation of the random phase approximation, and it should be compared with Eq. (3.31). It has only real eigenvalues if the eigenvalues of Eq. (3.31) are all positive, so that, if $|\Phi\rangle$ really minimizes the expectation value of the Hamiltonian, the solutions of these equations represent stable oscillations of the determinant about its equilibrium value. If, however, $|\Phi\rangle$ does not minimize the expectation value of the Hamiltonian, but only makes it stationary (at a saddle point or maximum), then Eq. (5.76) may have eigenvalues with negative imaginary parts, and Eq. (5.75) shows that a mode of this sort grows spontaneously until it has a large amplitude, when our approximation to the time-dependent Hartree-Fock equations breaks down. Solutions of the stationary Hartree-Fock equations which do not minimize the expectation value of the Hamiltonian are therefore characterized by the fact that collective motion about such solutions is likely to be unstable.

The small amplitude approximation may break down even if the motion is not unstable but if Eq. (5.76) has an eigenvalue zero. In this case there is no restoring force for a certain collective mode, so its amplitude may grow linearly with time. For example, there is no restoring force for a localized wave function which moves uniformly in space without change of form, or for a wave function without spherical symmetry which rotates with uniform angular velocity. Therefore the time-dependent Hartree-Fock theory gives a semiclassical picture of translational and rotational motion as well as of vibrational motion.

11. Application to the shell model

The methods we have developed in the previous two sections can be applied to finite systems as well as to infinite systems. We can take, as a particular example, a spherical nucleus with no nucleons outside filled shells, such as Ca^{40}. Although we know that the actual nuclear forces are unsuitable for use in the Hartree-Fock theory, we can calculate with some effective potential such as the one suggested by Skyrme (1959). We are interested in the excited states which are obtained by exciting one nucleon from a closed shell. To a first approximation, the energy of such a state is just the Hartree-Fock energy of the shell to which the particle is excited minus the Hartree-Fock energy of the shell where it was before excitation. If we take account of the interactions by using the methods of Sec. 9, we find that the poles of the Green's function occur at the eigenvalues $\hbar\omega$ of Eq. (5.76). These poles give the eigenvalues of the Hamiltonian relative to the ground state energy. Equation (5.76) is a sort of modified Schrödinger equation whose solutions give the particle-hole excited states which are stationary when the interaction is taken into account. If there were no interaction, the eigenvalues would just be the shell-model energies $\epsilon_m - \epsilon_i$, but, in the presence of coupling, the energy levels are shifted.

Since the shell-model potential is spherically symmetric, the eigenfunctions of Eq. (5.76) must be eigenfunctions of angular momentum and parity. With charge-independent forces, they are also eigenfunctions of isotopic spin. Since the ground state of a light closed shell nucleus has isotopic spin zero (the wave function is symmetric between protons and neutrons), the particle-hole excited states must have isotopic spin zero or unity. If the protons and neutrons are excited with the same phase the isotopic spin is zero, and if they are excited with opposite phase, the isotopic spin is unity. It has been shown by Brown et al. (1961) that the levels with isotopic spin zero lie below the unperturbed shell-model levels, while those with isotopic spin unity lie above the shell-model levels.

The levels with angular momentum unity, odd parity, and isotopic spin unity have been studied by Brown and Bolsterli (1959). They show that the coupling should raise one of these levels far above the others, and that the raised level should be the only one connected to the ground state by a substantial matrix element of the electric dipole operator. This theory shows the connection between the collective description of the giant dipole resonance due to Goldhaber and Teller (1948) and its description in terms of the shell model, due to Wilkinson (1956). Wilkinson suggested that the resonance is due to the fact that one particle in a closed shell nucleus can be excited by an electric dipole photon in many different ways, but all these excitations have approximately the same energy. The method of Brown and Bolsterli shows that these possible excitations are coupled together in such a way that only one combination absorbs the photon, and it explains why the resonance occurs at a higher energy than we should expect from the shell model. The equation used by Brown and Bolsterli is not identical to Eq. (5.71), since they ignore the term which couples X_{mi} to Y_{mi}. Figures 21(a) and (b) are allowed for, but not Fig. 21(c).

The levels with zero isotopic spin are depressed by the coupling, and it seems that one level is likely to come much lower than all the others with the same quantum numbers. The level with angular momentum unity and odd parity is a spurious level, corresponding to a translation of the nucleus; the energy given by Eq. (5.76) for this level is zero. The levels with angular momentum two and even parity and with angular momentum three and odd parity are quadrupole and octupole vibrational states of the nucleus, which are indeed observed at low energies. We can see how these low levels occur by taking the matrix elements in Eq. (5.76) to be equal to a constant V. Eq. (5.76) reduces to

$$(\epsilon_m - \epsilon_i - z_0)X_{mi} = -V\sum_{j=1}^{N}\sum_{n=N+1}^{\infty}(X_{nj} + Y_{nj}),$$

$$(\epsilon_m - \epsilon_i + z_0)Y_{mi} = -V\sum_{j=1}^{N}\sum_{n=N+1}^{\infty}(X_{nj} + Y_{nj}), \qquad (5.77)$$

so that the eigenvalues z_0 are given by

$$\sum_{i=1}^{N}\sum_{m=N+1}^{\infty}2(\epsilon_m - \epsilon_i)/[(\epsilon_m - \epsilon_i)^2 - z_0^2] = -1/V. \qquad (5.78)$$

If we plot the left hand side of this equation as a function of z_0, we get the curve shown in Fig. 22. The function goes to infinity where z_0 is equal to plus or minus one of the shell model energies. The roots of the equation are given by the intersection of the curve with a horizontal line at a level $-1/V$. If V is positive, one root lies above all the shell model levels, and if V is quite small and negative, one root lies below all the shell model levels. If the shell model levels are all close together, this one root may be some distance from the other roots, which all lie close to the shell model levels. If V is so large and negative that the

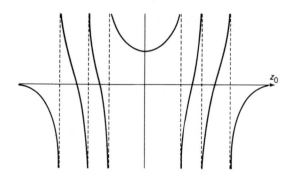

FIG. 22. A plot of the left hand side of Eq. (5.78). Points on the curve with ordi-
nate $-1/V$ have abscissas that give plus or minus the energy of excited states
in the random phase approximation.

left hand side of Eq. (5.78) for $z_0 = 0$ is greater than $-1/V$, then
there are two imaginary roots and the excitation is unstable.

The analysis of particle-hole excited states in nuclei can be helped by
the use of certain sum rules discussed by Sachs and Austern (1951).
These sum rules have the form

$$\sum_n |\langle \Psi_0 | Q | \Psi_n \rangle|^2 (E_n - E_0) = \tfrac{1}{2} \langle \Psi_0 | [Q, [H, Q]] | \Psi_0 \rangle, \qquad (5.79)$$

where Q is a one-particle Hermitian operator. The states which occur
in the sum on the left hand side are particle-hole excitations, since Q
operates on only one particle. The double commutator whose expectation value occurs on the right hand side may be quite a simple operator
or even a number, so that the right hand side can often be evaluated
more easily than the left. If Q is the electric dipole operator

$$Q = e \int \rho^{(p)}(r)(z - z_0) d^3r, \qquad (5.80)$$

where z_0 is the z-component of the centre of mass, then the double
commutator of Q with the kinetic energy operator is

$$[Q, [T, Q]] = -(e^2\hbar^2/2MA^2)$$

$$\times [(\sum_{i=1}^{Z} Nz_i - \sum_{i=Z+1}^{A} Zz_i), [\sum_{i=1}^{A} \partial^2/\partial z_i^2, (\sum_{i=1}^{Z} Nz_i - \sum_{i=Z+1}^{A} Zz_i)]]$$

$$= NZe^2\hbar^2/MA. \qquad (5.81)$$

Here e is the proton charge, M the nucleon mass, Z the proton number,
N the neutron number, and A the mass number. If the potential were
local and had no charge exchange part, it would commute with Q, and

so the right hand side of Eq. (5.79) would be $NZe^2\hbar^2/2MA$. The experimental fact that the left hand side, measured by gamma-ray absorption, is greater than this has been used by Levinger and Bethe (1950) to estimate the amount of charge exchange (which does not commute with Q) in the nucleon-nucleon potential. One of the advantages of the random phase approximation is that, if it is used to estimate the left hand side of Eq. (5.79), it generally gives a much better result than the unperturbed shell model. In fact, it gives the number which the right hand side would give if $|\Psi_0\rangle$ were replaced by the Hartree-Fock ground state wave function. This is an example of the principle that a calculation based on the properties of the Green's functions is more likely to preserve sum rules and dispersion relations than a calculation which ignores them.

The articles of Mottelson, Lipkin, and Bohm in "The Many-Body Problem" (published by Methuen, London, 1959) have more detailed treatments of some of the topics discussed in this chapter.

VI. Statistical Mechanics and Superconductivity Theory

1. The partition function

In the previous chapter we have considered excited states of many-particle systems which have energies only slightly greater than the ground state energy. For example, the energy of a quantum of zero sound with a particular momentum does not increase as the volume of the Fermi liquid increases, but it remains constant. All the other forms of excitation we considered have energies which either remain constant or decrease as the volume of the system increases. If we consider an excitation energy which is proportional to the extent of the system, we have to take account of a very large number of possible excitations, a number which increases exponentially with the extent of the system. It is obviously useless to try and describe such excitations exactly, and the methods of statistical mechanics must be used. In this way we can attempt to calculate the average properties of the excited states.

To study quantum mechanical systems, it is generally convenient to use the *grand canonical ensemble*, for which the energy of the system and the number of particles are not required to have definite values, but only particular average values. The thermodynamic properties of a system can all be deduced from the behaviour of the grand canonical *partition function*, which is equal to

$$Z = \sum_n \exp(\alpha N_n - \beta E_n), \qquad (6.1)$$

where N_n is the number of particles in the stationary state n, E_n is the energy of the state, and the sum goes over all stationary states of the system. It is assumed that the system is confined to a volume $\mathcal{v}$. Since

95

the relative probability of the state n is exp $(\alpha N_n - \beta E_n)$, the average energy of the system is

$$\bar{E} = \sum_n E_n \exp (\alpha N_n - \beta E_n)/\sum_n \exp (\alpha N_n - \beta E_n)$$

$$= -[\partial (\log Z)/\partial \beta]_\alpha, \tag{6.2}$$

and the average number of particles is

$$\bar{N} = [\partial (\log Z)/\partial \alpha]_\beta. \tag{6.3}$$

The parameter β is $(\kappa T)^{-1}$, where κ is the Boltzmann constant and T is the temperature, and α is equal to $\beta\mu$, where μ is the chemical potential. The other thermodynamic functions can be calculated quite simply.† The quantity which can be most directly calculated from the grand canonical partition function is the pressure, which is given by

$$p\mathcal{V} = \kappa T \log Z$$

$$= TS + \mu\bar{N} - \bar{E}. \tag{6.4}$$

We call $-p\mathcal{V}$ the *thermodynamic potential*, and this is the quantity that we usually try to calculate. The entropy is S in this formula.

The grand canonical partition function is a sum of elements of the operator

$$\psi = \exp(\alpha N - \beta H), \tag{6.5}$$

which is called the *distribution function*. The relation

$$Z = \sum_n \langle \Psi_n | \psi | \Psi_n \rangle = \text{Tr } \psi \tag{6.6}$$

remains true in any representation, and so it is very useful for the development of quantum statistical mechanics. Since the number operator N commutes with the Hamiltonian H, the distribution function satisfies the equation

$$\partial \psi/\partial \beta = -H\psi. \tag{6.7}$$

This equation is known as the Bloch equation, and it is very similar to the Schrödinger equation for the wave function, with $it/\hbar$ replaced by β. This formal analogy between the wave function and the distribution function is exploited in several ways. We shall find that almost any method that can be applied to the study of the ground state of a many-particle system can also be used for determining its properties at finite temperatures. No essentially new methods are introduced, but the methods developed in the previous four chapters are adapted to finite

† See L. Landau and E. Lifshitz, "Statistical Physics," pp. 68–71 and 105–107, Addison-Wesley, Reading, Massachusetts, 1958, for details.

temperature problems. In the earlier chapters we applied the methods to nuclear physics and to the theory of liquid He³, and in the following chapters we shall study the properties of electrons in metals and in plasmas at finite temperatures. From our point of view, the most interesting phenomenon in this field is the occurrence of superconductivity in many metals at very low temperatures. The techniques which have been developed to explain this phenomenon can also be used in nuclear physics, and they suggest that liquid He³ might also be superfluid at a sufficiently low temperature. Both these applications are considered in this chapter.

2. Free fermions and bosons

We can easily work out the partition function for a system of noninteracting fermions or bosons. If the creation and annihilation operators are $a_i{}^\dagger$ and a_i, for a level i with energy ϵ_i, the distribution function is

$$\psi = \exp\left[\sum_i (\alpha a_i{}^\dagger a_i - \beta \epsilon_i a_i{}^\dagger a_i)\right]$$

$$= \prod_i \exp\left[(\alpha - \beta \epsilon_i) a_i{}^\dagger a_i\right]. \tag{6.8}$$

In any many-fermion configuration, the level i is either unoccupied or occupied, and the trace of ψ is found by adding up all possible combinations. Therefore we get from Eq. (6.6)

$$Z = \prod_i [1 + \exp(\alpha - \beta \epsilon_i)]. \tag{6.9a}$$

For a system of bosons, the level i can be occupied by 0, 1, 2, or any number of particles, and so the partition function is

$$Z = \prod_i \{1 + \exp(\alpha - \beta \epsilon_i) + \exp[2(\alpha - \beta \epsilon_i)] + \cdots\}$$

$$= \prod_i [1 - \exp(\alpha - \beta \epsilon_i)]^{-1}. \tag{6.9b}$$

Substituting these expressions in Eqs. (6.4), (6.3), and (6.2), we get

$$p\mathcal{V} = \pm \kappa T \sum_i \log\left[1 \pm \exp(\alpha - \beta \epsilon_i)\right],$$

$$\bar{N} = \sum_i [\exp(\beta \epsilon_i - \alpha) \pm 1]^{-1},$$

$$\bar{E} = \sum_i \epsilon_i [\exp(\beta \epsilon_i - \alpha) \pm 1]^{-1}, \tag{6.10}$$

where the upper sign is for fermions and the lower sign for bosons.

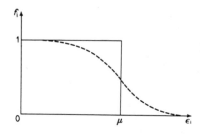

FIG. 23. Occupation number f_i of energy levels in a Fermi gas plotted as a function of energy ϵ_i. The solid curve gives the function at zero temperature, the broken curve at a finite temperature.

These are familiar results which can be obtained in a more direct manner, and which are discussed in the text-books.† At very low temperatures, the probability of occupation of a level in a fermion system becomes unity if ϵ_i is less than $\mu = \alpha/\beta$, and zero if ϵ_i is greater than μ. As the temperature rises the distribution becomes smoother. The probability of occupation f_i is shown as a function of ϵ_i for zero temperature and for a finite temperature in Fig. 23. At finite temperatures, μ may be either greater or less than the energy of the lowest level.

For bosons, the situation is entirely different, since

$$f_i = [\exp(\beta\epsilon_i - \alpha) - 1]^{-1}$$

must be positive for all i, and so μ cannot be greater than the lowest energy level. If the particles are phonons or photons, whose number is not conserved, μ is equal to zero. Suppose, however, that we consider free bosons whose number is conserved: the number per unit volume is

$$\frac{\bar{N}}{\upsilon} = \frac{1}{2\pi^2} \int_0^\infty \frac{k^2 dk}{\exp(\beta k^2/2M - \alpha) - 1}, \qquad (6.11)$$

which is a well-behaved integral tending to a finite limit as α tends to zero from below, since the integrand is always less than $2M/\beta$. In the limit $\alpha = 0$, the integral tends to a constant times $(2M/\beta)^{3/2}$, and, if α is less than zero, the integral is less than this. At first sight it would seem that, at a particular temperature, the density cannot exceed this limit. This is false, however, since the occupation of the lowest level increases indefinitely as α tends to zero, so any number of particles may be in this level. It is not legitimate to replace the sum in Eq. (6.10) by the integral of Eq. (6.11). If the density is higher than the maximum value of Eq. (6.11), a finite fraction of the particles must have zero momentum and be in the lowest energy level.

This condensation of particles in the zero momentum state, the Bose-Einstein condensation, was suggested by Einstein (1924, 1925). It has

† See for example, L. Landau and E. Lifshitz, "Statistical Physics," pp. 152-179, Addison-Wesley, Reading, Massachusetts, 1958.

been suggested that, as the temperature at which it would occur for noninteracting bosons with the mass of He^4 atoms and at the density of liquid helium is 3.2°, it might explain the transition of liquid helium to a superfluid state, which occurs at 2.2°. This matter has been carefully studied by London (1938). There is indeed a phase transition for noninteracting bosons, but the specific heat has only a discontinuous slope, whereas it is observed that the specific heat of liquid helium rises rapidly near the transition temperature, with an apparent logarithmic singularity at the transition temperature (Fairbank and co-workers, 1958). Also, a system of noninteracting particles would not be superfluid. We discuss how the interactions change this situation in Chapter X. Nothing similar occurs for free fermions, although the superconductivity of metals resembles superfluidity in some ways. The theory of superconductivity, which we discuss at some length here, shows that there is a formal relation between the two phenomena, although the physical pictures are quite different.

Since we need the formulae at a later stage, we write down the modifications to Eq. (6.10) which are necessary when the particles are photons or phonons, bosons whose number is not conserved. Firstly, since the number is not conserved, α must be put equal to zero. Secondly, there is a zero-point energy. Since this is everywhere infinite for photons it is usually ignored, but it has physical consequences for a system of phonons, and so should be included. The effect of these two modifications is to change Eq. (6.10) to

$$p\mathcal{U} = -\kappa T \sum_i \log \left[2 \sinh\left(\tfrac{1}{2}\beta\epsilon_i\right) \right],$$

$$\bar{N} = \sum_i \left[\exp(\beta\epsilon_i) - 1 \right]^{-1},$$

$$\bar{E} = \sum_i \tfrac{1}{2}\epsilon_i \coth\left(\tfrac{1}{2}\beta\epsilon_i\right), \qquad (6.11a)$$

as can be seen by making the appropriate modifications to Eq. (6.9b).

3. Superconductivity

The properties of the electrons in a superconducting metal are very different from the properties of noninteracting fermions, and for a long time it was difficult to see how these properties could be explained. A critical discussion of this problem was given by Feynman (1957), who suggested, correctly, that the simplest property to explain would be the specific heat at low temperatures. The specific heat of a gas of noninteracting fermions is proportional to the temperature, and the observed specific heat of a metal which is not a superconductor is indeed proportional to the temperature at sufficiently low temperatures. The specific heat of the electrons in a superconductor appears to vary like an exponential of minus the inverse temperature, instead of varying linearly; this can be measured by subtracting the specific heat of the phonons, which is proportional to the cube of the temperature, from the total specific heat of the metal. The exponential behaviour of the specific heat suggests that there is an *energy gap*, and that the lowest excited state of the electrons in a superconductor is separated from the ground state by a finite amount which is independent of the total extent of the system. The lowest excited state of a gas of noninteracting fermions lies indefinitely close to the ground state, since a fermion with momentum just less than the Fermi momentum can be excited to just above the Fermi surface with the expenditure of very little energy. Various other measurements, such as measurements of the absorption of microwave radiation, have confirmed the existence of an energy gap (Biondi *et al.*, 1958).

Another very important clue to the nature of superconductivity is the *isotope effect*, discovered experimentally by Maxwell (1950), and by Reynolds and associates (1950), and independently predicted on theoretical grounds by Fröhlich (1950). If the critical temperature at which superconductivity occurs is measured for different isotopes of the same metal, the critical temperature is found to be proportional to the mass number of the isotope. This shows that the crystal lattice must be an important part of the mechanism, and confirms Fröhlich's conjecture that the attractive force between electrons due to the exchange of phonons between them is responsible for superconductivity. We discuss this idea in more detail later.

The explanation of other properties of superconductors is expected to follow once we have understood the energy gap. The most striking property is the very high electrical conductivity of superconductors, such that currents may persist in a ring of superconducting metal for days. Closely connected with this is the Meissner effect; if there is a magnetic field inside a superconducting metal above the transition temperature, the field is completely expelled from the metal when it is cooled and becomes superconducting. Superconductivity is destroyed by a sufficiently high magnetic field, and the metal reverts to the "normal" state. In the absence of a magnetic field, the specific heat is discontinuous at the critical temperature, but there is no latent heat, and the specific heat appears to remain finite. Reviews of the properties of superconductors have been given in the "Handbuch der Physik" articles by Serin (1956) and Bardeen (1956).

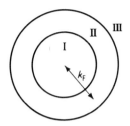

FIG. 24. The three regions of momentum space used in the model of a superconductor.

4. Model of the superconducting state

Before we discuss the theory of superconductivity proposed by Bardeen *et al.* (1957), we consider a model of a superconductor based on this theory which has been proposed by Wada and associates (1958), and by Anderson (1958). This is a very unrealistic model, but it has the advantage that it can be solved exactly, and that its solution displays most of the simpler properties of a superconductor.

We divide momentum space into three regions, separated by two spherical surfaces centred on the origin, as shown in Fig. 24. In the regions I and III, the energy of a level i is ϵ_i, and there is no interaction of the particles in these regions. In the region II, we assume that all levels have the same kinetic energy T, and that there is an interaction by which particles of opposite spin and momentum scatter against one another, with a constant matrix element for the interaction. The Hamiltonian for this region is

$$
\begin{aligned}
H_{\mathrm{II}} &= \sum_i T(a_{i+}{}^\dagger a_{i+} + a_{-i-}{}^\dagger a_{-i-}) + J\sum_i\sum_j a_{i+}{}^\dagger a_{-i-}{}^\dagger a_{-j-}a_{j+} \\
&= T\sum_i (a_{i+}{}^\dagger a_{i+} + a_{-i-}{}^\dagger a_{-i-}) + J\Big(\sum_i a_{i+}{}^\dagger a_{-i-}{}^\dagger\Big)\Big(\sum_i a_{i-}a_{i+}\Big),
\end{aligned}
$$

$$(6.12)$$

where a_{i+} is the annihilation operator for a particle with momentum i and spin in some specified direction which we call up, and a_{-i-} is the annihilation operator for a particle with momentum $-i$ and spin down. The sum goes over all values of the momentum in region II. Since there is no interaction of particles in regions I and III, these play a passive role, and we do not have to worry about them. The Fermi momentum is assumed to lie in the region II, so that almost all the levels in region I are occupied, and almost all the levels in region III are unoccupied.

Although this is a very unrealistic model of the electrons in a superconducting metal, there is a physical system for which it makes much more sense. For a nucleus, in which the region I contains all the filled shell, region III contains all the empty shells, and the region II is a partly filled shell, this is a more reasonable model. It may be a good approximation to neglect configuration mixing, in which case the regions I and III would play a passive role. Since all the nucleons in region II are in the same shell, they all have the same energy. If the forces between nucleons are short-range, the matrix elements of the potential which scatter nucleons of exactly opposite angular momentum are much larger than the other matrix elements. In this form, the problem was solved by Racah (1949) long before the application to superconductivity theory was considered.

We observe that if a pair of levels (levels with opposite spin and momentum) is occupied by only one particle at some time, it remains singly occupied. There is no second particle for the one particle to scatter against, and no pair of particles can scatter into the levels, because of the exclusion principle. These unpaired particles are also passive, like the particles in regions I and III, and the sums in Eq. (6.12) can be taken to exclude all such half-filled pairs of levels.

We write the operator that annihilates both particles in a pair of levels as

$$\beta_i = a_{-i-}a_{i+}. \tag{6.13}$$

This operator satisfies the relations

$$[\beta_i, \beta_j] = 0,$$

$$\beta_i{}^2 = \beta_i{}^{\dagger 2} = 0,$$

$$[\beta_i, \beta_j{}^\dagger] = 0, \qquad \text{for } i \neq j,$$

$$\beta_i\beta_i{}^\dagger + \beta_i{}^\dagger\beta_i = (1 - n_{i+})(1 - n_{-i-}) + n_{i+}n_{-i-} = 1. \tag{6.14}$$

This last relation only holds if both levels of the pair are occupied, or if both are unoccupied, but it does not hold for half-filled pairs of levels. These relations are the relations satisfied by the spin operators for different particles with angular momentum $\tfrac{1}{2}\hbar$, if we write

$$1 - n_{i+} - n_{-i-} = 2s_{zi},$$

$$\beta_i = s_{xi} + is_{yi},$$

$$\beta_i{}^\dagger = s_{xi} - is_{yi}. \tag{6.15}$$

Using the algebra of the spin operators we get

$$\beta_i{}^\dagger\beta_i = (s_{xi} - is_{yi})(s_{xi} + is_{yi})$$

$$= \tfrac{1}{2} - s_{zi}, \tag{6.16}$$

and so the Hamiltonian in the region II' (the region II with the half-filled pairs of levels excluded) becomes

$$
\begin{aligned}
H_{\mathrm{II'}} &= T\sum_i (1 - 2s_{zi}) + J\Big[\sum_i (s_{xi} - is_{yi})\Big]\Big[\sum_i (s_{xi} + is_{yi})\Big] \\
&= T(B - 2S_z) + J(S_x - iS_y)(S_x + iS_y) \\
&= T(B - 2S_z) + J[(S_x^2 + S_y^2 + S_z^2) - (S_z^2 + S_z)], \quad (6.17)
\end{aligned}
$$

where B is the number of pairs of levels in the region II. We have used the fact that the sum of these "spin" operators gives another angular momentum operator with components S_x, S_y and S_z, which we call the total spin. In the same way we find that the number operator for the region II' is

$$
N_{\mathrm{II'}} = 2\sum_i \beta_i{}^\dagger \beta_i = B - 2S_z. \qquad (6.18)
$$

We have replaced the original problem of particles interacting by means of a pairing force by an equivalent problem of fixed particles with spin one half coupled together in such a way that the Hamiltonian (6.17) involves only the total spin of the system. If the spin of one of the particles in this new problem is up, the corresponding pair of levels in the old problem is unoccupied, and, if the spin is down, the corresponding pair of levels is occupied, as can be seen from Eq. (6.15). We diagonalize both the number operator (6.18) and the Hamiltonian (6.17) if we diagonalize both S_z and $(S_x^2 + S_y^2 + S_z^2)$. Since the latter operator is just the square of the total spin, which commutes with S_z, the two can be diagonalized simultaneously. The z-projection of the total spin must be an integer or half-integer, according to whether B is even or odd, and $(S_x^2 + S_y^2 + S_z^2)$ must be equal to $S(S + 1)$, where S is an integer or half-integer not less than $|S_z|$ and not greater than $\frac{1}{2}B$. The total number of particles in the region II' of the original problem determines S_z, and so the energy is determined by S.

If the spins are all parallel or all antiparallel to the z-axis, S_z is $\pm\frac{1}{2}B$, and S must equal $\frac{1}{2}B$. There are B ways of making $S_z = \pm(\frac{1}{2}B - 1)$; one of these ways has total spin $\frac{1}{2}B$, so $B - 1$ must have total spin $\frac{1}{2}B - 1$. We can continue this argument in the same way, since there are in general

$$B!/r!(B - r)!$$

ways of making $S_z = \pm(\frac{1}{2}B - r)$, so that there are this number of ways of making $S \geq (\frac{1}{2}B - r)$. The number of ways of making $S = \frac{1}{2}(B - r)$ is therefore

$$
\frac{B!}{r!(B - r)!} - \frac{B!}{(r - 1)!(B - r + 1)!} = \frac{B!(B - 2r + 1)}{r!(B - r + 1)!}. \qquad (6.19)
$$

This number is the degeneracy of a level whose energy is, from Eqs. (6.17) and (6.18),

$$E = DT + J[(\tfrac{1}{2}B - r)(\tfrac{1}{2}B - r + 1) - (\tfrac{1}{2}B - D)(\tfrac{1}{2}B - D + 1)]$$
$$= DT + J[D(B - D + 1) - r(B - r + 1)], \qquad (6.20)$$

where $2D$ is the number of particles in the region II'.

We have now found a complete solution of the original problem. If the strength of the interaction J is positive the ground state is highly degenerate and has very little potential energy. We are interested, however, in the situation when the potential is attractive, with J negative, so that the ground state is the nondegenerate state with $r = 0$, and this has energy

$$E_0 = TD + JD(B - D + 1). \qquad (6.21)$$

The first excited state is separated from this by an energy

$$E_1 - E_0 = -JB, \qquad (6.22)$$

and this is a degenerate state. The levels go up to zero potential energy with slowly decreasing spacing and rapidly increasing degeneracy. The quantum number r is one half of the quantum number that is called *seniority* in nuclear physics. The name "seniority" is used because an energy level with a particular seniority only occurs if there are at least that number of particles in the unfilled shell.

We expect a nondiagonal matrix element of the interaction between two electrons in a metal to be inversely proportional to the volume, so J is inversely proportional, while B and D are directly proportional. Hence the potential energy of the ground state, given by Eq. (6.21), is proportional to the volume. The energy gap between the ground state and the first excited state, given by Eq. (6.22), is independent of the volume. This is just the result required to explain the exponential behaviour of the specific heat of a superconductor at very low temperatures. There are other ways of making an excitation from the ground state, such as by breaking up a pair, but all these processes require an energy independent of the total volume.

The expression for the grand canonical partition function in the region II is

$$Z_{II} = \sum_{q=0}^{K} \sum_{r=0}^{\frac{1}{2}(K-q)} \sum_{D=r}^{K-q-r} \frac{2^q K!(K - q - 2r + 1)}{q!r!(K - q - r + 1)!}$$
$$\times \exp\{\beta[(\mu - T)(q + 2D) - JD(K - q - D + 1)$$
$$+ Jr(K - q - r + 1)]\}, \qquad (6.23)$$

where $2K$ is the number of levels in the region II, and q is the number of half-filled pairs of levels. The logarithm of the summand in this expression is

$$q \log 2 + K \log K - q \log q - r \log r - (K - q - r) \log(K - q - r)$$
$$+ \beta(\mu - T)(q + 2D) - \beta JD(K - q - D) + \beta Jr(K - q - r), \quad (6.24)$$

if we keep only those terms which are proportional to the volume. This expression has a maximum at

$$q = \tfrac{1}{2}K \operatorname{sech}^2 \theta,$$

$$r = \tfrac{1}{4}K(1 - \tanh \theta)^2,$$

$$D = -J^{-1}(\mu - T) + \tfrac{1}{2}(K - q),$$

$$4\theta = -\beta JK \tanh \theta. \quad (6.25)$$

We are particularly interested in the case $\mu = T$. In the limit of large volume, we can take the sum on the right of Eq. (6.23) to be equal to its largest term. The equation for θ in Eq. (6.24) has one positive solution if $-\beta JK$ is greater than four. For large β (low temperature), the maximum lies inside the tetrahedral volume allowed for q, r and D, but, as β approaches the value

$$\beta_C = -4/JK, \quad (6.26)$$

the maximum approaches the edge of the tetrahedron at the point $q = 2r = 2D = \tfrac{1}{2}K$, and it remains at this point at higher temperatures. The number of particles, equal to $2D + q$, is always K for this value of μ. One interesting feature of this model is that above the transition temperature given by Eq. (6.26) the thermodynamic functions are all independent of J. The thermodynamic properties of the system therefore give no indication of the transition until it actually occurs, when there is a discontinuity in the specific heat.

The contributions of regions I and III to the partition function are independent of the situation in region II, and so they should simply be multiplied by the contribution (6.23) of the region II. The thermodynamic functions for regions I and III, which contain noninteracting fermions, should be added to the thermodynamic functions for the region II to obtain the thermodynamic functions of the whole system. The details of this model have been discussed by Thouless (1960).

5. Superconducting state of a real metal

A real metal differs very greatly from the model we discussed in the last section, but the differences do not seem to be sufficient to destroy the value of the model. The main differences are that the electrons are not free, but move in the periodic field of the ions, the kinetic energy is not constant in region II, but varies in the usual way, the interaction is not just a simple attractive potential with a constant matrix element, and the interaction is not confined to particles of exactly opposite momentum.

The effect of the lattice structure of the metal has not been studied in any detail, but there is no reason to believe that it makes necessary any fundamental changes in the theory. The problem is particularly difficult because those metals that have a simple band structure, such as the alkali metals, are not superconducting. The main effects of the periodic structure are to change the effective number of free electrons and to alter the single-particle spectrum. Both these effects can be allowed for by determining the Fermi surface and the effective mass of the electrons from other experimental evidence on the metal, but no basic change in the theory is necessary.

The variation of the single-particle energy in the region II of Fig. 24 is allowed for in the theory of Bardeen et al. (1957), but the solution found is no longer exact, except possibly in the limit of an infinite volume. This is not a serious drawback, and the theory does agree with the exact solution in the appropriate limit. The spin model of Wada and associates (1958) and Anderson (1958) enables the solution to be understood in a simple manner. If Eq. (6.12) for the Hamiltonian is replaced by the more general

$$H_{\text{II}} = \sum_i \epsilon_i(a_{i+}{}^\dagger a_{i+} + a_{-i-}{}^\dagger a_{-i-}) + J\left(\sum_i a_{i+}{}^\dagger a_{-i-}{}^\dagger\right)\left(\sum_i a_{-i-}a_{i+}\right), \tag{6.27}$$

we can use the substitutions given by Eq. (6.15) to get

$$H_{\text{II}'} = \sum_i \epsilon_i(1 - 2s_{zi}) + J[S(S + 1) - S_z(S_z + 1)]$$

$$= \sum_i \epsilon_i(1 - 2s_{zi}) + J\sum_i (S_x s_{xi} + S_y s_{yi} - s_{zi}),$$

$$N_{\text{II}'} = \sum_i (1 - 2s_{zi}). \tag{6.28}$$

We want to find the ground state of this system for which N has a particular value, so we try to minimize $H_{\text{II}'} - \mu N_{\text{II}'}$. Each spin is acted on by a field whose x and y components are constant and proportional to $-JS_x$ and $-JS_y$, and whose z component is $2(\epsilon_i - \mu) + J$, which varies from one spin to another.

If the spin problem were a classical problem, it would be simple to solve, since the spins would line up parallel to the field. There is a self-consistency problem, since the equation

$$s_{xi}:s_{yi}:s_{zi} = -JS_x:-JS_y:2(\epsilon_i - \mu) + J \qquad (6.29)$$

implies that

$$J\sum_i[J^2S_x^2 + J^2S_y^2 + (2\epsilon_i - 2\mu + J)^2]^{-1/2} = 1. \qquad (6.30)$$

We expect a similar solution to be good even though the spins are quantized. The projection of the spin i in the direction given by Eq. (6.29) should be one half. The spin, however, precesses about this direction, and it is only if we can ignore fluctuations due to the precession that the solution is good. We must notice that S_z also fluctuates, so $N_{\mathrm{II}'}$ has not been exactly diagonalized in this solution. These fluctuations are generally of order $\sqrt{N}$, and can probably be ignored for a large system.

There is a spurious degeneracy of the ground state given by Eqs. (6.29) and (6.30), since there is nothing to determine S_x and S_y separately, but only $S_x^2 + S_y^2$ is determined. Any orientation of the projection of the total spin in the xy plane gives the same energy. In order to diagonalize S_z, a linear combination of all these possible orientations must be taken; the degeneracy is therefore connected only with the fluctuation of the total number of particles in the solution, and it is not connected with any physical degeneracy.

This type of approximate solution, which does not give a precise total number of particles, is much more easily understood at finite temperatures, where it can be regarded as giving a good approximation to the properties of the grand canonical ensemble. To test the accuracy of the approximation we appeal to the variational principle. In the next section we discuss a form of the variational principle that can be used at finite temperatures.

The real interaction between electrons in a metal is not fully known, but some qualitative features can be deduced. The repulsive Coulomb potential between electrons is fully known, of course, and in momentum space it has matrix elements $4\pi e^2/q^2\mathcal{V}$, where $\hbar q$ is the change in momentum of one of the particles. The electrons also interact with the lattice, but the form of this interaction is difficult to determine, and it is not easy to take the interaction fully into account. The method originally suggested by Bloch (1928) and used by Fröhlich (1950) is to ignore the lattice except as a mechanism for producing an additional interaction between electrons. The exchange of a phonon between two electrons produces an attractive force, just as the exchange of a meson between two nucleons produces an attractive force. A phonon can carry a large momentum, comparable with the Fermi momentum, but it has an energy small compared with the Fermi energy, since the Debye temperature of a metal is about 10^2 degrees, while the Fermi temperature is 10^4 degrees or more. Because of the low energy of the phonons, they can most easily be emitted or absorbed by electrons close to the Fermi surface, so the change in electron energy across the region II of Fig. 24 should be of the order of magnitude of κ times the Debye temperature, which is the maximum energy of the phonons. This argument is presented in more detail in Chapter IX, Sec. 3. The matrix element should depend somewhat on the angle between the initial momentum of an electron and its final momentum, but the spherically symmetric part should be the most important part. The assumption of a constant attractive matrix element of the potential in region II is not good, but it is hard to find a more convincing approximation. A more complicated potential can, anyway, be handled in the Bardeen, Cooper, and Schrieffer theory. A study of the variation of the potential from metal to metal, based on the superconductivity data, has been made by Pines (1958).

The neglect of matrix elements of the potential other than those between particles of opposite momentum is an important approximation. If the problem is solved with complete neglect of these other matrix elements, and then their expectation value is determined, this expectation value is found to be small. These elements do seem to make a qualitative change in the excitation spectrum, and they may introduce "collective" excited states, or *excitons*, into the energy gap for some systems. This question has been discussed by Anderson (1958) and by Bogoliubov and co-workers (1958).

6. The variational principle for the partition function

In Chapter III, we showed how use can be made of the fact that the ground state energy is less than or equal to the expectation value of the Hamiltonian given by a trial wave function. There is a similar theorem which applies to the equilibrium state of a system at finite temperatures. This theorem was originally proved by Peierls (1938), but we use here a proof due to Schultz (1958).

Suppose that we have a continuous function $f(x)$ that is concave upwards, so that

$$f(x') \geq f(x) + (x' - x)f'(x). \tag{6.31}$$

We have an operator Q whose complete set of eigenstates we denote by k, where the eigenvalue is Q_k, and we have an arbitrary complete set of orthogonal states denoted by n, whose scalar products with the eigenstates of Q we denote by a_{nk}. From Eq. (6.31) we have

$$f(Q_k) \geq f(Q_{nn}) + (Q_k - Q_{nn})f'(Q_{nn}), \tag{6.32}$$

so that it follows that

$$[f(Q)]_{nn} = \sum_k |a_{nk}|^2 f(Q_k)$$

$$\geq \sum_k |a_{nk}|^2 f(Q_{nn}) + \sum_k |a_{nk}|^2 (Q_k - Q_{nn})f'(Q_{nn})$$

$$= f(Q_{nn}). \tag{6.33}$$

Summing over the complete set of sets n, we get

$$Tr\, f(Q) \geq \sum_n f(Q_{nn}). \tag{6.34}$$

We can take as a special case $f(x) = \exp(\beta x)$ and $Q = \mu N - H$, so that, using Eqs. (6.6) and (6.5), we get

$$Z = Tr \, \exp\left[\beta(\mu N - H)\right]$$

$$\geq \sum_n \exp\left[\beta(\mu N_{nn} - H_{nn})\right], \tag{6.35}$$

where the sum goes over any set of orthogonal states. If the set is not complete, the inequality is even stronger.

7. Quasiparticle method

We can apply this theorem to the solution of the superconductivity problem given by Eqs. (6.29) and (6.30), or, rather, the corresponding solution at finite temperatures. In the equivalent spin problem, this solution is a semiclassical solution, in which the spins are quantized parallel to some "field" which varies from spin to spin. The way to achieve this varying direction of quantization is to replace the particle annihilation operators by the *quasiparticle*† annihilation operators

$$\alpha_{i0} = x_i^* a_{i+} - y_i a_{-i-}^\dagger,$$

$$\alpha_{i1} = x_i^* a_{-i-} + y_i a_{i+}^\dagger, \tag{6.36}$$

where

$$|x_i|^2 + |y_i|^2 = 1. \tag{6.37}$$

These new operators satisfy anticommutation relations similar to those

† Note that the word "quasiparticle" is used with rather different meanings here and in Chapter V.

satisfied by the particle creation and annihilation operators, and the anticommutation relations are

$$\{\alpha_{i0}, \alpha_{j0}\} = \{\alpha_{i0}, \alpha_{j1}\} = \{\alpha_{i0}, \alpha_{j1}{}^\dagger\} = \text{etc.} = 0,$$

$$\{\alpha_{i0}, \alpha_{j0}{}^\dagger\} = \delta_{ij},$$

$$\{\alpha_{i1}, \alpha_{j1}{}^\dagger\} = \delta_{ij}. \tag{6.38}$$

If the spins in the equivalent problem that we discussed in Sec. 4 are quantized along the z-axis, a_{i+} and a_{-i-} give zero when they operate on a state with the spin of i up, and $a_{i+}{}^\dagger$ and $a_{-i-}{}^\dagger$ give zero when they operate on a state with the spin of i down. There is a certain direction such that, if the spins are quantized along this new direction, α_{i0} and α_{i1} give zero when they operate on a state with the spin of i up, and $\alpha_{i0}{}^\dagger$ and $\alpha_{i1}{}^\dagger$ give zero when they operate on a state with the spin of i down. This new direction has components

$$2 \operatorname{Re} (x_i y_i), \qquad 2 \operatorname{Im} (x_i y_i), \qquad |x_i|^2 + |y_i|^2$$

in the original coordinate system, as can be shown by combining Eqs. (6.15) and (6.36). If $|\Psi'\rangle$ is any state for which the particle level i is unoccupied, the state

$$|\Psi\rangle = (x_i{}^* + y_i a_{i+}{}^\dagger a_{-i-}{}^\dagger) |\Psi'\rangle \tag{6.39}$$

has the quasiparticle level i unoccupied, since α_{i0} and α_{i1} both give zero when they operate on this state. States in which the quasiparticle level i is occupied can be obtained by operating on Eq. (6.39) with α_{i0} or α_{i1}. This quasiparticle method was introduced by Bogoliubov et al. (1957) and by Valatin (1958), but it is equivalent to the method used by Bardeen and associates (1957).

The semiclassical solution of the spin problem ignores correlations between different spins once the direction of quantization for each spin has been chosen; the direction is determined by the direction of the field which acts on the spin. The equivalent approximation is to ignore correlations in the occupation of different quasiparticle levels once the coefficients of the transformation (6.36) have been chosen. The coefficients are determined from the variational principle, but the same result could be obtained from the spin model.

At first we only allow interaction between particles of opposite spin and momentum, but we take the matrix element of the potential between a configuration with the levels $[j, +]$ and $[-j, -]$ occupied and a configuration with the levels $[i, +]$ and $[-i, -]$ occupied to be an arbitrary matrix V_{ij}. We can rewrite the Hamiltonian minus μ times the number operator in terms of the quasiparticle operators defined by Eq. (6.36) as

$$H - \mu N = \sum_i (\epsilon_i - \mu)(a_{i+}^\dagger a_{i+} + a_{-i-}^\dagger a_{-i-})$$

$$+ \sum_i \sum_j V_{ij} a_{i+}^\dagger a_{-i-}^\dagger a_{-j-} a_{j+}$$

$$= \sum_i (\epsilon_i - \mu)[2|y_i|^2 + (|x_i|^2 - |y_i|^2)(\alpha_{i0}^\dagger \alpha_{i0} + \alpha_{i1}^\dagger \alpha_{i1})$$

$$+ 2x_i{}^* y_i \alpha_{i0}^\dagger \alpha_{i1}^\dagger + 2x_i y_i{}^* \alpha_{i1} \alpha_{i0}]$$

$$+ \{\sum_i \sum_j V_{ij} x_i{}^* y_i{}^* [x_j y_j - x_j y_j(\alpha_{j0}^\dagger \alpha_{j0} + \alpha_{j1}^\dagger \alpha_{j1})$$

$$+ x_j^2 \alpha_{j1} \alpha_{j0} - y_j^2 \alpha_{j0}^\dagger \alpha_{j1}^\dagger] + \text{Hermitian conjugate}\}$$

$$+ \sum_i \sum_j V_{ij} B_i{}^\dagger B_j - \sum_i \sum_j V_{ij} x_i{}^* y_i{}^* x_j y_j, \quad (6.40)$$

where

$$B_i = a_{-i-} a_{i+} - x_i y_i$$

$$= -x_i y_i (\alpha_{i0}^\dagger \alpha_{i0} + \alpha_{i1}^\dagger \alpha_{i1}) + x_i^2 \alpha_{i1} \alpha_{i0} - y_i^2 \alpha_{i0}^\dagger \alpha_{i1}^\dagger. \quad (6.41)$$

Since the matrix element V_{ij} is proportional to $\mathcal{U}^{-1}$, we can neglect terms like $\sum_i V_{ii}$ in comparison with terms like $\sum_i (\epsilon_i - \mu)$. The diagonal part of the right hand side of Eq. (6.40) is

$$(H - \mu N)_D = \sum_i (\epsilon_i - \mu)[2|y_i|^2 + (|x_i|^2 - |y_i|^2)(n_{i0} + n_{i1})]$$

$$+ \sum_i \sum_j V_{ij} x_i{}^* y_i{}^* x_j y_j (1 - n_{i0} - n_{i1})(1 - n_{j0} - n_{j1}) \quad (6.42)$$

where n_{i0} and n_{i1} are the number operators for quasiparticles. We are unable exactly to evaluate the trace of the exponential of this operator, so we restrict ourselves to those configurations in which a particular proportion of the quasiparticle levels in each region of momentum space are occupied. We are therefore assuming that correlations between quasiparticles are unimportant. We assume that $(n_{i0} + n_{i1})$ is two with probability f_i and zero with probability g_i. The expectation value of $H - \mu N$ in such a configuration is

$$\langle (H - \mu N) \rangle = \sum_i (\epsilon_i - \mu)[1 + (|x_i|^2 - |y_i|^2)(f_i - g_i)]$$

$$+ \sum_i \sum_j V_{ij} x_i{}^* y_i{}^* x_j y_j (f_i - g_i)(f_j - g_j). \quad (6.43)$$

Suppose that momentum space is divided into cells with w_α pairs of quasiparticle levels in each cell, so that $f_\alpha w_\alpha$ pairs of levels in a cell are doubly occupied, $(1 - f_\alpha - g_\alpha)w_\alpha$ are singly occupied, and $g_\alpha w_\alpha$ are unoccupied. The number of different configurations that have this property is

$$\prod_\alpha \frac{w_\alpha! 2^{w_\alpha(1-f_\alpha-g_\alpha)}}{(w_\alpha f_\alpha)!(w_\alpha g_\alpha)![(1-f_\alpha-g_\alpha)w_\alpha]!}.$$

The trial value for z is this number times the exponential of $-\beta$ times Eq. (6.43). The logarithm of this number multiplied by the Boltzmann constant κ gives the trial value for the entropy S. We have

$$ST = -\kappa T \sum_i \{ f_i \log f_i + g_i \log g_i$$

$$+ (1 - f_i - g_i) \log \left[\tfrac{1}{2}(1 - f_i - g_i)\right]\}. \quad (6.44)$$

Equation (6.43) gives the trial value for $\bar{E} - \mu\bar{N}$, and Peierls' theorem, Eq. (6.35), tells us that the difference between the right hand sides of Eqs. (6.44) and (6.43) gives a rigourous lower bound for $p\upsilon = \mu\bar{N} + ST - \bar{E}$. Partial differentiation of this difference with respect to f_i and g_i gives us equations that must be satisfied for the expression to have its highest possible value, which are

$$-\kappa T\{\log f_i - \log\left[\tfrac{1}{2}(1-f_i-g_i)\right]\} = (\epsilon_i - \mu)(|x_i|^2 - |y_i|^2)$$

$$+ 2 \operatorname{Re} \sum_j V_{ij} x_i {}^* y_i {}^* x_j y_j (f_j - g_j),$$

$$-\kappa T\{\log g_i - \log[\tfrac{1}{2}(1-f_i-g_i)]\} = -(\epsilon_i - \mu)(|x_i|^2 - |y_i|^2)$$

$$- 2 \operatorname{Re} \sum_j V_{ij} x_i {}^* y_i {}^* x_j y_j (f_j - g_j). \quad (6.45)$$

Adding these two equations together, we get

$$4f_i g_i = (1 - f_i - g_i)^2, \quad (6.46)$$

so that we can write

$$f_i = \tfrac{1}{4}[1 - \tanh\left(\tfrac{1}{2}\beta\nu_i\right)]^2,$$

$$g_i = \tfrac{1}{4}[1 + \tanh\left(\tfrac{1}{2}\beta\nu_i\right)]^2,$$

$$1 - f_i - g_i = \tfrac{1}{2}\operatorname{sech}^2\left(\tfrac{1}{2}\beta\nu_i\right), \quad (6.47)$$

where ν_i is determined from Eq. (6.45) as

$$\nu_i = (\epsilon_i - \mu)(|x_i|^2 - |y_i|^2) - 2\operatorname{Re}\sum_j V_{ij} x_i {}^* y_i {}^* x_j y_j \tanh\left(\tfrac{1}{2}\beta\nu_j\right).$$

$$(6.48)$$

We can substitute Eq. (6.47) into Eqs. (6.44) and (6.43) and differentiate their difference with respect to $x_i{}^*$ and $y_i{}^*$, taking account of the subsidiary condition (6.37), in order to find the condition for $p\mathcal{V}$ to have its maximum value. We get

$$-(\epsilon_i - \mu)|x_i|^2 \tanh\left(\tfrac{1}{2}\beta\nu_i\right)$$
$$+ \sum_j V_{ij} x_i{}^* y_i{}^* x_j y_j \tanh\left(\tfrac{1}{2}\beta\nu_i\right) \tanh\left(\tfrac{1}{2}\beta\nu_j\right) = \lambda_i|x_i|^2,$$

$$(\epsilon_i - \mu)|y_i|^2 \tanh\left(\tfrac{1}{2}\beta\nu_i\right)$$
$$+ \sum_j V_{ij} x_i{}^* y_i{}^* x_j y_j \tanh\left(\tfrac{1}{2}\beta\nu_i\right) \tanh\left(\tfrac{1}{2}\beta\nu_j\right) = \lambda_i|y_i|^2, \quad (6.49)$$

which is satisfied by

$$|x_i|^2 - |y_i|^2 = (\epsilon_i - \mu)/\nu_i,$$
$$4|x_i y_i|^2 = 1 - (\epsilon_i - \mu)^2/\nu_i{}^2. \quad (6.50)$$

These equations can be rewritten by introducing the parameter $\Delta_i = 2x_i y_i \nu_i$, so that we have

$$x_i y_i = \Delta_i/2\nu_i,$$
$$|x_i|^2 - |y_i|^2 = (\epsilon_i - \mu)/\nu_i,$$
$$\nu_i{}^2 = (\epsilon_i - \mu^2) + |\Delta_i|^2, \quad (6.51)$$

and from, Eqs. (6.48) and (6.49),

$$\Delta_i = -\sum_j V_{ij}(\Delta_j/2\nu_j) \tanh\left(\tfrac{1}{2}\beta\nu_j\right), \quad (6.52)$$

We can interpret ν_i as the energy of the quasiparticle i. Firstly, the probability of single or double occupation of the quasiparticle level is the probability of a pair of fermion levels with energy $\mu + \nu_i$ each being singly or doubly occupied. Secondly, Eq. (6.43) shows that if one quasiparticle is added in the level i to the equilibrium distribution given by Eq. (6.47), $\bar{E} - \mu\bar{N}$ increases by

$$(\epsilon_i - \mu)(|x_i|^2 - |y_i|^2) + 2\,\mathrm{Re}\sum_j V_{ij} x_i{}^* y_i{}^* x_j y_j \tanh\left(\tfrac{1}{2}\beta\nu_j\right) = \nu_i, \quad (6.53)$$

according to Eq. (6.48).

We take the simple case $V_{ij} = -V_0/\mathcal{V}$ in a region close to the Fermi surface, and $V_{ij} = 0$ otherwise. The parameter Δ_i is then a constant in this region, according to Eq. (6.52), and we call this constant Δ the energy gap, since the lowest value of ν_i is Δ, according to Eq. (6.51). Equation (6.52) becomes

$$V_0 N(0) \int \frac{\tanh\left(\tfrac{1}{2}\beta\sqrt{(\epsilon - \mu)^2 + \Delta^2}\right)}{2\sqrt{(\epsilon - \mu)^2 + \Delta^2}} d\epsilon = 1, \quad (6.54)$$

where $N(0)$ is the density of states per unit energy range, equal to

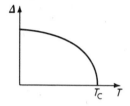

FIG. 25. Energy gap Δ as a function of temperature T

$Mk_F/2\pi^2\hbar^2$, where M is the effective mass of the electrons. We assume that $N(0)$ is constant, since the integration only goes over values of ϵ very close to μ. For the reasons given in Sec. 5, the limits of the integration are given by $|\epsilon - \mu|$ being of the order of $\kappa\Theta$, where Θ is the Debye temperature. The value of the integral depends logarithmically on the cut-off, since the hyperbolic tangent is very close to unity there.

The relation of this model to real superconductors and the comparison of its properties with their physical properties are discussed by Bardeen *et al.* (1957). The energy gap Δ given by Eq. (6.54) decreases steadily with temperature as shown in Fig. 25. At the critical temperature T_C, the energy gap is zero, so the critical temperature is given, according to Eq. (6.54), by

$$\tfrac{1}{2}V_0N(0)\int \tanh\left[\tfrac{1}{2}\beta_C(\epsilon - \mu)\right](\epsilon - \mu)^{-1}d\epsilon = 1. \qquad (6.55)$$

Above this temperature, there is no solution to Eq. (6.54) except the trivial solution $\Delta = 0$. This trivial solution always exists, but it does not give a maximum for $p\upsilon$ unless there is no nontrivial solution. If Δ_i is zero, either x_i or y_i must be zero, and so a quasiparticle is either the same as a hole or a particle in this case. However small $V_0N(0)$ is, there is always a solution to Eq. (6.55), since the integral is a monotonic function of β_C which tends linearly to zero as β_C goes to zero and diverges logarithmically as β_C goes to infinity.

Although the interaction between electrons that do not have exactly opposite momenta makes an important contribution to the ground state energy or to the pressure, it does not affect the nature of the transition strongly. Its expectation value in the normal state is almost the same as its expectation value in the superconducting state, as was shown by Bardeen *et al.* (1957). Thus, even though a theory that neglects these matrix elements of the potential must give a very bad approximation for the ground state energy, it may give a good approximation for the difference between the normal and superconducting states, and it is this difference that is easy to measure experimentally.

There is essentially only one free parameter in this theory, which is $V_0N(0)$. Most physical properties, such as the energy gap at zero temperature, the critical temperature, the critical field, etc., can be fitted fairly well with this one parameter. There are some difficulties that remain, but the general agreement of the theory with experiment is remarkably good. A review of the theory has been written by Bardeen and Schrieffer (1960).

8. Superfluidity of liquid helium three

The explanation of superconductivity suggests that other many-fermion systems might have a similar phase transition at low temperatures, if there is an attractive force between the particles. The direct solution of Eq. (6.52) with a general potential is not possible, but the equation can be cast in a variational form so that, if a trial wave function makes the expectation value of a certain quantity negative, then a transition must occur. It has not been found possible to satisfy the variational principle with a spherically symmetric Δ_i for liquid He³, because of the strong effect of the repulsive part of the potential, but a Δ_i with quadrupole symmetry (D-wave) has been found by Emery and Sessler (1960). A similar result has been obtained by a rather different argument by Brueckner and co-workers (1960b). The reason for this is that the D-wave penetrates the repulsive region of the potential less than the S-wave does. The transition temperature predicted is in the range 0.05 to 0.1 degrees, but the transition has not yet been observed experimentally, although He³ has been cooled to these temperatures. This may be due to the failure of the theory when the forces are as strong as they are in liquid He³, or it may be due to the inhibition of the transition by impurities; Anderson and Morel (1960) suggest that impurities should influence the transition temperature quite strongly when the effective attraction between atoms is in the D-state.

This predicted phase has some interesting properties which have been discussed by Anderson and Morel (1960). If the potential V_{ij} in Eq. (6.52) has rotational symmetry, as it has for liquid He³, the equation may have a spherically symmetric solution, in which Δ_i and ν_i do not depend on the angle of i. Such a solution depends only on the S-state part of the potential, since other parts average out, and so it is impossible if the D-state potential is to produce the transition. The most symmetry that the solution can have is axial symmetry; if ν_i is axially symmetric, the solutions of Eq. (6.52) must depend on the azimuthal angle φ like $\exp(im\varphi)$, and Eq. (6.51) shows that the ν_i that such a solution determines is indeed independent of the azimuthal angle. Anderson and Morel argue that Δ_i should vary like $\exp(2i\varphi)$ for He³, and should vanish in the direction of the symmetry axis. Since the modulus of Δ_i is the energy gap, the energy gap must vanish in this direction, but this does not destroy the superfluidity of the system. The ground state should have a finite angular momentum, just as does the ground state of a single domain of a ferromagnetic substance. Subsequent work has shown that this axially symmetric solution should not occur.

9. The effect of pairing on nuclear properties

It was shown in calculations by Mayer (1950) that short-range attractive forces between nucleons lead to the formation of stable pairs of particles with zero angular momentum. The mutual potential energy of two particles in the same shell-model level is four times as great if they are coupled together to give angular momentum zero as if they are coupled together to give angular momentum two, with a δ-function potential. Therefore nuclei with even numbers of protons and neutrons have ground states with zero angular momentum, and the angular momentum of a nucleus with an odd number of particles is equal to the shell-model angular momentum of the one unpaired neutron or proton. Thus the attractive interaction between nucleons is largely responsible for the simplicity of the shell model. The model we discussed in Sec. 4 is quite a good model of the nucleus, if configuration mixing can be ignored.

In fact, although it is reasonable to suppose that closed shell nuclei are more or less free from configuration mixing, the different shell-modle levels within a shell are quite close together, and configuration mixing must be important. Belyaev (1959) has used the quasiparticle techniques discussed in Sec. 7 to take account of the formation of pairs which extend through several levels. This technique is very convenient and leads to quite simple results, but the approximate ground state used, the quasiparticle vacuum, is a superposition of states with different numbers of particles, and this leads to some difficulty in the interpretation of the results. The effect of the pairing is to lower the energy of the ground state without affecting much the excited states, so that it is separated from the first excited state by an energy gap much greater than would be expected from the simple shell model. Because the energy levels are altered, various other properties are altered, as Belyaev shows; for example, the moment of inertia of a deformed nucleus is reduced. The most important effect of the pairing is to improve the independent "particle" model by increasing the spacing of energy levels, but the independent entities are quasiparticles rather than physical particles.

The divergence of the Brueckner K-matrix discussed in Chapter IV, Sec. 9, is closely related to this effect. Indeed, the reason for the divergence of the sum on the right hand side of Eq. (4.52) is the reason for Eq. (6.55) always to have a solution. It has been shown by Mills and associates (1959) that the ground state of nuclear matter should be superfluid with the observed nuclear forces.

In *The Many-Body Problem*, superconductivity theory is discussed by Schrieffer and Belyaev, its application to nuclear theory is discussed by Mottelson and Belyaev, and experimental aspects of superconductivity are discussed by Lynton.

VII. Perturbation Theory at Finite Temperatures

1. The Bloch equation

Perturbation theory is useful for studying systems in equilibrium at finite temperatures for much the same reasons as it is useful for studying the ground states of systems. It can be used for calculating the effect of a small external field applied to a system; it can be used for estimating how good is a particular approximation to the equilibrium state of a system; or it can be used for proceeding in a systematic manner from the known equilibrium state of a simple system to an expression for the unknown equilibrium state of a more complicated system. We have paid most attention to the last of these uses, but the other two are equally important.

To obtain a perturbation series at finite temperatures, we exploit the analogy between the Bloch equation (6.7) for the distribution function and the time-dependent Schrödinger equation for the wave function, or for the development operator (4.9). It is convenient to split up $H - \mu N$ into an unperturbed part and a perturbation

$$H - \mu N = H_0 + H_1. \tag{7.1}$$

Usually, no part of the number operator is included in the perturbation H_1, but, if we wish to estimate the accuracy of the Bardeen et al. (1957) theory of superconductivity, we shall have to treat part of the number operator as a perturbation, since the unperturbed Hamiltonian (6.42) does not commute with the number operator. The expansion analogous to Eq. (4.13) is

$$\exp(\beta H_0)\psi = 1 - \int_0^\beta \exp(H_0 u_1) H_1 \exp(-H_0 u_1) du_1$$

$$+ \int_0^\beta du_2 \int_0^{u_2} du_1$$

$$\times \exp(H_0 u_2) H_1 \exp(-H_0 u_2) \exp(H_0 u_1) H_1 \exp(-H_0 u_1) - \cdots$$

$$= \sum_{n=0}^\infty \frac{(-1)^n}{n!} \int_0^\beta \cdots \int_0^\beta$$

$$\times T[H_1(-iu_n) \cdots H_1(-iu_2) H_1(-iu_1)] du_1 \cdots du_n, \quad (7.2)$$

where the "time-dependent" operators in the interaction picture are defined by

$$H_1(-iu) = \exp(H_0 u) H_1 \exp(-H_0 u). \quad (7.3)$$

The time ordered product denoted by T is defined so that operators whose arguments have larger negative imaginary parts stand to the left of those with smaller negative imaginary parts in their arguments. We refer to the variable as "time" because of the analogy with the Schrödinger equation. It has, in fact, nothing to do with physical time, but is related to inverse temperature. We use the notation

$$Q(-iu) = \exp(H_0 u) Q \exp(-H_0 u),$$

$$\tilde{Q}(-iu) = \exp(H_0 u) Q^\dagger \exp(-H_0 u), \quad (7.4)$$

because $\tilde{Q}(-iu)$ is not the Hermitian conjugate of $Q(-iu)$, but rather of $Q(iu)$.

2. Linked graph expansion

The graphical techniques that were introduced in Chapter IV can also be used here. A method of using Wick's theorem to evaluate the partition function, calculated from Eqs. (6.6) and (7.2), was proposed by Matsubara (1955). The method can be applied to systems of interacting fermions and bosons, but we shall consider its application to a system of fermions interacting by two-body forces, with the Hamiltonian given by Eq. (4.19).

The operators that occur in the time-ordered product of Eq. (7.2) are products of creation and annihilation operators. In the interaction picture, the time-dependent annihilation operators defined by Eq. (7.4) are

$$a_k(-iu) = a_k \exp\left[-(\epsilon_k - \mu)u\right],$$

$$\tilde{a}_k(-iu) = a_k{}^\dagger \exp\left[(\epsilon_k - \mu)u\right], \tag{7.5}$$

where ϵ_k is the unperturbed energy of a particle with momentum k.

In Chapter IV we defined a normal product so that its "vacuum" expectation value is zero. We used Wick's theorem to break down a time-ordered product into a sum of contractions and normal products; the contractions are simply numbers, but the normal products have zero expectation value and give no contribution. To use the same method to evaluate $Z = \mathrm{Tr}\psi$ from the expansion given in Eq. (7.2), it is necessary to define a normal product in such a way that its average value is zero when each diagonal element is weighted with the factor $\exp(-\beta H_0)$. This is achieved by the trick of splitting each annihilation and creation operator that occurs in the time-ordered product into two parts,

$$a_k = (1 - g_k)\alpha_{1k} + g_k\alpha_{2k}{}^\dagger,$$

$$a_k{}^\dagger = (1 - g_k)\alpha_{1k}{}^\dagger + g_k\alpha_{2k}, \tag{7.6}$$

where g_k is a real number. This is not a canonical transformation like Eq. (6.36), but α_{1k} and $\alpha_{2k}{}^\dagger$ are each exactly the same operator as a_k. The only purpose of this splitting is to define the normal product suitably. The normal product of a number of creation and annihilation operators is found by making the substitution (7.6), and reordering the operators so that all the $\alpha_1{}^\dagger$ operators come to the left, next come the $\alpha_2{}^\dagger$ operators, next the α_2 operators, and to the right come the α_1 operators. There is a change of sign for each permutation. Once the reordering has been done, α_{1k} and $\alpha_{2k}{}^\dagger$ may be replaced by a_k, and $\alpha_{1k}{}^\dagger$ and α_{2k} may be replaced by $a_k{}^\dagger$.

First we must show that a normal product defined in this way does have the average value zero. We have to sum over all diagonal matrix elements, with the weighting factor

$$\exp(-\beta H_0) = \exp\left[-\beta \sum_k (\epsilon_k - \mu)a_k{}^\dagger a_k\right].$$

Each level can be either occupied or unoccupied, and the ratio of the weighting factors in these two cases is $\exp\left[-\beta(\epsilon_k - \mu)\right]$. Each level gives an independent factor, for a single product of creation and annihilation operators referring to different levels, so we need only consider a normal product of operators that all create or annihilate a particle in the same level. Unless the number of creation operators equals the number of annihilation operators, all the diagonal elements of the product vanish. In the case of one creation operator and one annihilation operator, we have

$$N[a_k{}^\dagger a_k] = (1 - g_k{}^2)\alpha_{1k}{}^\dagger \alpha_{1k} + g_k(1 - g_k)\alpha_{2k}\alpha_{1k}$$
$$+ (1 - g_k)g_k\alpha_{1k}{}^\dagger \alpha_{2k}{}^\dagger - g_k{}^2\alpha_{2k}{}^\dagger \alpha_{2k}$$
$$= (1 - g_k{}^2)a_k{}^\dagger a_k - g_k{}^2 a_k a_k{}^\dagger. \tag{7.7}$$

The average value of this vanishes if we choose

$$g_k{}^2 = f_k = \{\exp[\beta(\epsilon_k - \mu)] + 1\}^{-1} = \tfrac{1}{2}\{1 - \tanh[\tfrac{1}{2}\beta(\epsilon_k - \mu)]\}, \tag{7.8}$$

which is the probability of the level k being occupied in the unperturbed system. To prove that the normal product vanishes if there are more than two operators referring to the same level, we can make use of the fact that a normal product changes sign if two of the fermion operators that occur in it are interchanged. We therefore have

$$N[a_k{}^\dagger a_k{}^\dagger a_k a_k] = -N[a_k{}^\dagger a_k{}^\dagger a_k a_k] = 0, \tag{7.9}$$

and similarly for normal products of more than four operators referring to the same level.

The contraction of two operators is defined as the difference between their normal product and their time-ordered product, and is a number. The contraction of two creation or of two annihilation operators vanishes, and the contraction of an annihilation and a creation operator is, from Eqs. (7.5), (7.7), and (7.8),

$$a_k(t_2){}^\bullet \tilde{a}_{k'}(t_1){}^\bullet = T[a_k(t_2)\tilde{a}_{k'}(t_1)] - N[a_k(t_2)\tilde{a}_{k'}(t_1)]$$
$$= \begin{cases} (1 - f_k)\delta_{kk'}\exp[(\epsilon_k - \mu)(t_1 - t_2)], & \text{for } t_1 < t_2, \\ -f_k\delta_{kk'}\exp[(\epsilon_k - \mu)(t_1 - t_2)], & \text{for } t_1 \geq t_2. \end{cases} \tag{7.10}$$

Comparison of this with Eqs. (4.28) and (4.29) show that at finite temperatures a level k behaves like an occupied level with probability f_k and like an unoccupied level with probability $1 - f_k$.

Using Wick's theorem, we can get a graphical representation of the perturbation series for Z which is very similar to the representation of the perturbation series for $\langle \Phi_0 | U(t) | \Phi_0 \rangle$ discussed in Chapter IV. We draw all possible graphs with vertices between zero and β. We get a factor equal to a matrix element of the interaction from each vertex, a factor given by Eq. (7.10) for a fermion line, and a factor -1 from each closed loop of fermion lines.

Again we can exploit the fact that unlinked parts of a graph contribute independent factors. The sum of all graphs is equal to the exponential of the sum of all linked graphs. The perturbation series for the pressure is therefore, according to Eq. (6.4), given by the sum of all linked graphs A discussion of this method has been given by Bloch and De Dominicis (1958). A similar method has been derived by Montroll and Ward (1958), and the relation between the two methods is discussed by Bloch and De Dominicis (1959).

3. Comparison with ground state perturbation theory

There is a remarkable similarity between the form of perturbation theory that is used for finding the ground state energy and this finite temperature perturbation theory, but there are some important differences. In order to compare these expansions, we consider the first and second order terms in the perturbation series. Some of the graphs that contribute to these two terms are shown in Fig. 26. There are also other graphs derived from these by changing the sides at which lines enter or leave a vertex, related to these graphs as Fig. 5(b) is related to Fig. 5(a), or as Figs. 6(b), (c) and (d) are related to Fig. 6(a). Figure 26(c) shows a graph that does not occur in ground state perturbation theory, since the same level cannot be both a hole level and a particle level. At finite temperatures, however, $f_{k'}(1 - f_{k'})$ does not vanish, so there is a contribution from this graph. The contribution of graphs like Fig. 26(a) to $\log Z$ is

$$- \tfrac{1}{2}\beta \sum_{k} \sum_{k'} f_k f_{k'} (V_{kk',kk'} - V_{kk',k'k}). \tag{7.11}$$

The contribution of graphs like Fig. 26(b) is

$$\tfrac{1}{2} \sum_{k} \sum_{k'} \sum_{k''} \sum_{k'''} V_{kk',k''k'''} (V_{k''k''',kk'} - V_{k''k''',k'k})(1 - f_k)(1 - f_{k'})f_{k''}f_{k'''}$$

$$\times \int_0^\beta dt_2 \int_0^{t_2} dt_1 \exp\left[(\epsilon_k + \epsilon_{k'} - \epsilon_{k''} - \epsilon_{k'''})(t_1 - t_2)\right]$$

$$= \tfrac{1}{2} \sum_{k} \sum_{k'} \sum_{k''} \sum_{k'''} V_{kk',k''k'''} (V_{k''k''',kk'} - V_{k''k''',k'k})$$

$$\times \left[\beta \frac{(1 - f_k)(1 - f_{k'})f_{k''}f_{k'''}}{\epsilon_k + \epsilon_{k'} - \epsilon_{k''} - \epsilon_{k'''}} \right.$$

$$\left. + \frac{f_k f_{k'}(1 - f_{k''})(1 - f_{k'''}) - (1 - f_k)(1 - f_{k'})f_{k''}f_{k'''}}{(\epsilon_k + \epsilon_{k'} - \epsilon_{k''} - \epsilon_{k'''})^2} \right]$$

$$= \tfrac{1}{2}\beta \sum_{k} \sum_{k'} \sum_{k''} \sum_{k'''} V_{kk',k''k'''} (V_{k''k''',kk'} - V_{k''k''',k'k})$$

$$\times \frac{(1 - f_k)(1 - f_{k'})f_{k''}f_{k'''}}{\epsilon_k + \epsilon_{k'} - \epsilon_{k''} - \epsilon_{k'''}}. \tag{7.12}$$

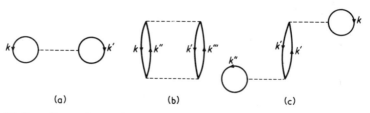

FIG. 26. Some first and second order graphs in finite temperature perturbation theory.

This is similar in structure to Eq. (4.36). The contribution of graphs like Fig. 26(c) is

$$\tfrac{1}{2}\beta^2 \sum_k \sum_{k'} \sum_{k''} f_k f_{k'} (1 - f_{k'}) f_{k''}$$

$$\times (V_{kk',kk'} - V_{kk',k'k})(V_{k'k'',k'k''} - V_{k'k'',k''k'}). \quad (7.13)$$

This term is the one with no analogue in ground state perturbation theory.

It has been observed by Kohn and Luttinger (1960) that the ground state perturbation expansion can be obtained by allowing the temperature to tend to zero, if the volume of the system is finite. The propagators given by Eqs. (7.10) and (7.8) have the propagators given by Eqs. (4.28) and (4.29) as their limit when β tends to infinity. The parameter μ must be set equal to the unperturbed Fermi energy in the ground state theory, and then the unperturbed number of particles in the new theory is equal to the number of particles in the old theory. The change in the number of particles due to the perturbation can be found from Eq. (6.3), but this tends to zero as the temperature tends to zero, since μ occurs only in the factors f_k, and their derivatives with respect to μ tend exponentially to zero. The only terms which remain in the perturbation series for $\log Z$ are those which are linear in β, and these lead to exactly the same expression for the energy as we derived earlier.

The situation may be quite different if we allow the volume to become infinite before we take the zero temperature limit. The parameter μ can no longer be set equal to the unperturbed Fermi energy, but it must be identified with the chemical potential. Every graph that contributes to the ground state energy in the ground state theory contributes the same amount to

$$- \kappa T \log Z = \bar{E} - \mu \bar{N} \quad (7.14)$$

in the zero-temperature limit of the finite temperature theory. The two calculations are not identical, however, since in the one case the number of particles is given, and the energy is calculated, while in the other case the chemical potential is given and the quantity (7.14) is calculated. The difference must be due to those graphs like Fig. 26(c) that contribute only in the finite-temperature theory and give zero in the ground state theory. In the limit of zero temperature the expression (7.13) tends to a finite limit, since

$$\beta f_{k'}(1 - f_{k'}) = \tfrac{1}{4}\beta \operatorname{sech}^2 \left[\tfrac{1}{2}\beta(\epsilon_{k'} - \mu)\right]$$

behaves like a δ-function of $\epsilon_{k'} - \mu$ in this limit.

The results given by these two forms of perturbation theory are not necessarily identical. Indeed, a counterexample has been constructed by Kohn and Luttinger (1960) in which the two series give different results for the energy. It has, however, been shown by Luttinger and Ward (1960) that there are some circumstances under which the series are identical. There are two possible reasons for a discrepancy. One is that the unperturbed ground state may be orthogonal to the true ground state, so that the first form of the theory gives the energy of some other stationary state, as can be seen from Eq. (4.31). The other possible reason is that the poor convergence of the perturbation series may make the order of the limiting processes important. In any case it serves as a warning against taking the results of perturbation theory too seriously.

The difference between ground state perturbation theory and finite temperature perturbation theory is illustrated by the increased complication of the Hartree-Fock theory. Although plane wave states satisfy the Hartree-Fock equations at finite temperatures, this is not the whole story, since there is an additional self-consistency condition on the occupation numbers of the levels. Since the probability that a level of energy ϵ_k is occupied is $\tfrac{1}{2}\{1 - \tanh\left[\tfrac{1}{2}\beta(\epsilon_k - \mu)\right]\}$, the equation for the self-consistent energy is

$$\epsilon_k = T_k + \tfrac{1}{2}\sum_{k'}(V_{kk',kk'} - V_{kk',k'k})\{1 - \tanh\left[\tfrac{1}{2}\beta(\epsilon_{k'} - \mu)\right]\}, \quad (7.15)$$

where T_k is the kinetic energy of the level. This is quite a complicated equation, and, even in the limit of zero temperature it differs from the usual Hartree-Fock equations; whereas any determinant of plane waves satisfies Eq. (3.7), Eq. (7.15) requires that the occupied levels should all have lower energies than the unoccupied levels. The Hartree-Fock expression for the pressure allows for graphs like Figs. 26(a) and (c), and also for many more complicated graphs, whereas the Hartree-Fock expression for the energy at zero temperature allows only for the graphs of Fig. 5.

4. Expectation value of an operator

We can use finite temperature perturbation theory to calculate the expectation value of an operator in a system in thermal equilibrium. To show this, we use the relation

$$\langle Q \rangle = \{ \sum_n \exp [-\beta(E_n - \mu N_n)] Q_{nn} \} / \sum_n \exp [-\beta(E_n - \mu N_n)]$$

$$= \text{Tr} \{ Q \exp [-\beta(H - \mu N)] \} / \text{Tr} \{ \exp [-\beta(H - \mu N)] \}. \quad (7.16)$$

We now define a function of a parameter γ by

$$z(\gamma) = \text{Tr} \exp [-\beta(H - \mu N + \gamma Q)]. \quad (7.17)$$

This function is equal to the partition function for $\gamma = 0$, and its derivative at $\gamma = 0$ gives the expectation value of Q, since Eqs. (7.17) and (7.16) show that

$$[\partial \log z(\gamma) / \partial \gamma]_{\gamma=0} = -\beta \langle Q \rangle. \quad (7.18)$$

The function $z(\gamma)$ is just the partition function we should have if the Hamiltonian H were replaced by $H + \gamma Q$. The logarithm of this partition function could be calculated by summing all linked graphs if, as well as the normal perturbation H_1, we were to take into account an additional interaction γQ. However, we do not want to know $\log z(\gamma)$ completely, but we only need to know its derivative at $\gamma = 0$, according to Eq. (7.18). This must be given by the sum of all those linked graphs that contain the interaction γQ just once. This prescription for calculating the expectation value of an operator is the same as the prescription in ground state perturbation theory, and the graphs which occur for one- and two-particle operators include those shown in Figs. 8 and 9.

5. Classical limit of perturbation theory

The expansion of the partition function is much more difficult in quantum mechanics than in classical mechanics. In classical mechanics the kinetic energy and the potential energy separate, so that the partition function can be written as a product of a factor which comes from the kinetic energy only and a factor which comes from the potential energy only. The evaluation of the factor that involves the kinetic energy is straightforward, and it is only the potential energy part for which approximate methods must be used. An expansion for the free energy was derived by Mayer (1937), and a simple derivation of the method has recently been given by Salpeter (1958). This method leads to the "virial expansion" of the pressure as a power series in the density.

If quantum effects are unimportant, this classical expansion is much simpler to use than the expansion we have discussed in the earlier part of this chapter. Quantum corrections can be included by using the method of Kahn and Uhlenbeck (1938), which gives the partition function as a power series in $\hbar^2$. Although the derivation of the classical theory from the quantum theory is less satisfying than its derivation from first principles, it does help to clarify our understanding of the quantum theory; the relation between the two expansions has been briefly discussed by Bloch and De Dominicis (1959). Conversely, the quantum theory can be derived by reordering the expansion given by Kahn and Uhlenbeck; this is the method used by Lee and Yang (1959a).

We can obtain the classical limit of the expansion by treating Planck's constant $\hbar$ as a variable parameter, which we allow to tend to zero while we keep the temperature and density constant. If we consider the unperturbed system, the density of particles is

$$\bar{N}/\mathcal{V} = \mathcal{V}^{-1}\sum_k f_k$$

$$= \pi^{-2}\int_0^\infty \{\exp\left[\beta(\hbar^2 k^2/2M - \mu)\right] + 1\}^{-1} k^2 dk, \qquad (7.19)$$

and this tends to a finite limit as $\hbar$ tends to zero if μ is varied in such a way that exp $(\mu\beta)$ is proportional to $\hbar^3$. In this limit we get the usual Maxwell-Boltzmann distribution law. When we take the interaction into account, we still keep exp $(\mu\beta)$ proportional to $\hbar^3$. In the limit of small $\hbar$, the propagator defined by Eq. (7.10) is independent of k, unless $\beta\hbar^2 k^2/2M$ is of order unity. The factor contributed by a closed loop of fermion lines is independent of the coordinates of the vertices, and is just a power of exp $(\mu\beta)$ for each hole line in the loop. There must be at least one hole line in each closed loop.

We can transform the perturbation expansion so that it is written in configuration space instead of in momentum space. The propagators defined by Eq. (7.10) are independent of k, so they become proportional to δ-functions in configuration space. If the interaction is local, all the points on a closed loop must therefore refer to the same point in space. As we go round a closed loop, there is a δ-function for each line, and integration over all these points but one gives $\delta(0)$. This should, however, be replaced by something proportional to $\hbar^3$, since the propagator is only constant in momentum space for values of k much less than $(2M\kappa T)^{\frac{1}{2}}/\hbar$. We therefore get a finite contribution from those graphs that have only one hole line in each closed loop.

The closed loops of the quantum theory therefore reduce to the points of the classical cluster expansion, and the number of closed loops is equal to the order of the corresponding cluster integral. In the classical theory, a sum is made over all terms which have the same number of points to get the cluster integral. Such a summation over all graphs which have the same number of closed loops can be readily made only in the classical limit of the quantum theory, even in the simplest case of just two closed loops.

Finite temperature perturbation theory is discussed in *The Many-Body Problem* (Methuen, 1959) by Bloch and De Dominicis.

VIII. Green's Functions at Finite Temperatures

1. Excited states at finite temperatures

When we considered the excited states of systems in Chapter V, we observed that the problem of describing particular excited states is only of interest for finite systems, since the energy levels of infinite systems are too numerous for us to consider any of them individually. This argument is even stronger when we study excitations of a system in equilibrium at a finite temperature, since even the equilibrium state is a statistical ensemble of a very large number of energy levels. All we can hope to study are the general features of the most numerous types of excited states.

We may be concerned either with macroscopic excitations of the system, or with microscopic excitations. It is possible by imposing external conditions to move the system as a whole; we could, for example, give the container of a fluid a uniform translational motion. This type of macroscopic excitation can be handled theoretically by calculating the partition function as

$$\text{Tr} \left[\exp \left(\alpha N - \beta H + \gamma P \right) \right],$$

where P is the momentum operator, and then choosing γ so that it gives the required average translational motion. This is a standard technique in statistical mechanics.

In another type of macroscopic excitation, one part of the system may be excited relative to another part; the average velocity may vary from one point in the system to another, or the temperature may vary, for example. In general, this type of excitation is very difficult to handle, since the system is not in equilibrium. It may be that the macroscopic variables change so slowly that there is approximate thermodynamic equilibrium at each point, and that the return of the system to equilibrium can be described in terms of dissipative processes such as viscosity and heat conduction. The calculation of such quantities as the coefficient of viscosity and the thermal conductivity is therefore an important aspect of the theory of many-particle systems at finite temperatures. The theory of such dissipative processes is generally known as transport theory.

The other type of excitation with which we are concerned is an excitation which is obtained by adding one or two particles or holes to the system in equilibrium. For example, one of the simplest ways of exciting a system in equilibrium is to add one particle to it without disturbing any of the particles that were there before. The system is then no longer in equilibrium, but it will soon return to equilibrium, with its temperature and density almost unchanged. In the theory of the ground state of a many-particle system, we defined a single-particle Green's function to describe the behaviour of this sort of excitation, and it is possible to define a similar Green's function which describes this sort of excitation at finite temperatures.

The single-particle Green's function which is used at finite temperatures is just the average of Green's functions defined by an equation like Eq. (5.1). In the energy representation it is

$$S_k(t_1 - t_2)$$

$$= \frac{\{\sum_n \exp\left[\beta(\mu N_n - E_n)\right]\langle\Psi_n|\, T\left[a_k(t_2)\tilde{a}_k(t_1)\right]|\Psi_n\rangle\}}{\sum_n \exp\left[\beta(\mu N_n - E_n)\right]}$$

$$= \mathrm{Tr}\,\{\exp\left[\beta(\mu N - H)\right]T\left[a_k(t_2)\tilde{a}_k(t_1)\right]\}/\mathrm{Tr}\,\exp\left[\beta(\mu N - H)\right]. \quad (8.1)$$

It is convenient to measure energies from the chemical potential, so that the time-dependent operators are defined by

$$a_k(t) = \exp\left[it(H - \mu N)\right]a_k \exp\left[-it(H - \mu N)\right],$$

$$\tilde{a}_k(t) = \exp\left[it(H - \mu N)\right]a_k{}^\dagger \exp\left[-it(H - \mu N)\right], \quad (8.2)$$

where t may be real or imaginary. In this time-dependent form, the Green's function measures how the system returns to equilibrium after the addition or subtraction of a particle. The Fourier transform of the Green's function is an average of terms like those of Eq. (5.15), and its imaginary part gives the change in the distribution of energy which is induced by the addition or removal of a particle.

The properties and uses of Green's functions at finite temperatures have been discussed by Bonch-Bruevich and Kogan (1960), who give references to their earlier work, and by Martin and Schwinger (1959).

2. Calculation of Green's functions by perturbation theory

The way to calculate a Green's function like the one defined by Eq. (8.1) becomes clear if we put $t_1 = -iu_1$, $t_2 = -iu_2$, where u_1 and u_2 are real numbers between zero and β. If we take the case $u_2 > u_1$, we have, from Eq. (8.1),

$$S_k(-iu_1 + iu_2) = \text{Tr } \{\exp\left[(u_2 - \beta)(H - \mu N)\right] a_k$$
$$\times \exp\left[(u_1 - u_2)(H - \mu N)\right] a_k{}^\dagger$$
$$\times \exp\left[-u_1(H - \mu N)\right]\}/\text{Tr} \exp\left[-\beta(H - \mu N)\right]. \quad (8.3)$$

It is possible to make series expansions of the exponentials in the numerator similar to the expansion given by Eq. (7.2), taking the limits of the integrations to be u_2 and β for the expansion of $\exp\left[(u_2 - \beta)(H - \mu N)\right]$, u_1 and u_2 for the expansion of $\exp\left[(u_1 - u_2)(H - \mu N)\right]$, and zero and u_1 for the expansion of $\exp\left[-u_1(H - \mu N)\right]$. We can then apply Wick's theorem to find the average value of each term in the product of these three expansions. The numerator must therefore be given by the sum of all graphs, linked or unlinked, which have all their vertices between zero and β, and which have an external line representing the level k which enters the graph at u_1 and leaves it at u_2. The denominator is given by the sum of all graphs which have no external lines, so the Green's function must be given as the sum of all linked graphs with one external line k. The prescription for calculating the Green's functions at finite temperatures if therefore similar to the prescription for calculating the Green's functions for the ground state; the limits of integration are different, and the unperturbed propagators are different.

The one-particle Green's function can be calculated in terms of the connected self-energy parts, and a formula similar to Eq. (5.35) can be obtained. It is more interesting, however, to repeat the calculation of Chapter V, Sec. 9, in which an expression for the two-particle Green's function was derived. This calculation is similar to the calculation of the one-particle Green's function.

The Green's function we wish to calculate is analogous to the function defined by Eq. (5.61), and is

$$G(k_2, k_1; k_3, k_4; -i(u_1 - u_2))$$

$$\begin{cases} \langle \exp\left[-(u_1 - u_2)(H - \mu N)\right] a_{k_1}{}^\dagger a_{k_2} \\ \qquad \times \exp\left[(u_1 - u_2)(H - \mu N)\right] a_{k_3}{}^\dagger a_{k_4} \rangle & \text{for} \quad u_1 < u_2, \\ \\ \langle \exp\left[(u_1 - u_2)(H - \mu N)\right] a_{k_3}{}^\dagger a_{k_4} \\ \qquad \times \exp\left[-(u_1 - u_2)(H - \mu N)\right] a_{k_1}{}^\dagger a_{k_2} \rangle & \text{for} \quad u_1 > u_2. \end{cases} \quad (8.4)$$

We can derive an integral equation for this function, which is

$$G(k_2, k_1; k_3, k_4; -iu)$$

$$= -S_{k_1}(iu) S_{k_2}(-iu) \delta_{k_1 k_4} \delta_{k_2 k_3} + S_{k_1}(0) S_{k_3}(0) \delta_{k_1 k_2} \delta_{k_3 k_4}$$

$$+ \sum_{k_5} \sum_{k_6} \int_0^\beta \int_0^\beta S_{k_1}(iu') S_{k_2}(-iu') \Gamma(k_2, k_1; k_5, k_6; -iu'' + iu')$$

$$\times [G(k_5, k_6; k_3, k_4; -iu + iu'') - S_{k_5}(0) S_{k_3}(0) \delta_{k_5 k_6} \delta_{k_3 k_4}] du' du'', \quad (8.5)$$

where Γ is given by the sum of all irreducible vertex parts; an irreducible vertex part is a connected graph with one external line entering and one external line leaving at both u' and u'' which cannot be broken into two such graphs by breaking two fermion lines at the same level. The argument leading to this equation is the same as the argument leading to Eq. (5.66). We can solve this equation if we assume that the single-particle Green's functions behave like those for free particles—this is the quasiparticle approximation. The integral equation then becomes

$$G(k_2, k_1; k_3, k_4; -iu) - S_{k_1}(0) S_{k_3}(0) \delta_{k_1 k_2} \delta_{k_3 k_4}$$

$$= \tfrac{1}{4}\{1 + \tanh\left[\tfrac{1}{2}\beta(\epsilon_{k_1} - \mu)\right]\}\{1 - \tanh\left[\tfrac{1}{2}\beta(\epsilon_{k_2} - \mu)\right]\}$$

$$\times \{\delta_{k_1 k_4} \delta_{k_2 k_3} \exp\left[u(\epsilon_{k_2} - \epsilon_{k_1})\right] - \sum_{k_5} \sum_{k_6} \int_0^\beta \int_0^\beta \exp\left[u'(\epsilon_{k_2} - \epsilon_{k_1})\right]$$

$$\times \Gamma(k_2, k_1; k_5, k_6; -iu'' + iu')[G(k_5, k_6; k_3, k_4; -iu + iu'')$$

$$- S_{k_5}(0) S_{k_3}(0) \delta_{k_5 k_6} \delta_{k_3 k_4}] du' du''. \quad (8.6)$$

We must also use the relation

$$G(k_2, k_1; k_3, k_4; iu) = G(k_2, k_1; k_3, k_4; -i\beta + iu) \qquad (8.7)$$

which follows directly from Eq. (8.4). The equation is most easily solved by an expansion as a Fourier series. Writing

$$G(k_2, k_1; k_3, k_4; -iu) - S_{k_1}(0) S_{k_3}(0) \delta_{k_1 k_2} \delta_{k_3 k_4}$$

$$= \sum_\nu G_\nu(k_2, k_1; k_3, k_4) \exp\left(2\pi i\nu u/\beta\right),$$

$$\Gamma(k_2, k_1; k_3, k_4; -iu) = \sum_\nu \Gamma_\nu(k_2, k_1; k_3, k_4) \exp\left(2\pi i\nu u/\beta\right), \qquad (8.8)$$

where the sum goes over all integral values of ν, we get

$$G_\nu(k_2, k_1; k_3, k_4) = \frac{1}{2\beta}\left\{\frac{\tanh\left[\tfrac{1}{2}\beta(\epsilon_{k_2} - \mu)\right] - \tanh\left[\tfrac{1}{2}\beta(\epsilon_{k_1} - \mu)\right]}{\epsilon_{k_2} - \epsilon_{k_1} - 2\pi i\nu/\beta}\right\}$$

$$\times \{\delta_{k_1 k_4} \delta_{k_2 k_3} - \beta \sum_{k_5} \sum_{k_6} \Gamma_\nu(k_2, k_1; k_5, k_6) G_\nu(k_5, k_6; k_3, k_4)\}. \qquad (8.9)$$

3. Plasma oscillations

In Chapter V, we discussed the equation for the Green's function of a system of fermions which interact through some potential. We found that if the matrix element of the potential tends to a finite limit as the momentum transfer tends to zero, the Green's function describes the excitation known as "zero sound". If we wish to apply the method to the electrons in a metal or in a plasma, the situation is very different, since the electrons are charged and interact with one another through the Coulomb potential. The matrix element of the Coulomb potential is $4\pi e^2/\mathcal{U}q^2$, where $\mathcal{U}$ is the volume of the system and $\hbar q$ is the difference in momentum between the initial and final states of one of the two interacting electrons. Here we study the effect of this potential which has a singularity for zero momentum transfer.

We use the first order perturbation theory expression for the vertex part, which is given by Eq. (5.70), since this will give us the main effect of the singularity, so that we have

$$\Gamma_\nu(k + q, k; k' + q, k') = 4\pi e^2/\mathcal{U}q^2 - 4\pi e^2/\mathcal{U}(k - k')^2. \quad (8.10)$$

We consider the solution of Eq. (8.9) for small values of the momentum transfer, and we neglect the exchange term in Eq. (8.10). Equation (8.9) then becomes

$$G_\nu(k + q, k; k' + q, k')$$
$$= \frac{1}{2\beta}\left\{\frac{\tanh\left[\frac{1}{2}\beta(\epsilon_{k+q} - \mu)\right] - \tanh\left[\frac{1}{2}\beta(\epsilon_k - \mu)\right]}{\epsilon_{k+q} - \epsilon_k - 2\pi i\nu/\beta}\right\}$$
$$\times \left\{\delta_{kk'} - \frac{4\pi e^2\beta}{\mathcal{U}q^2}\sum_{k''}G_\nu(k'' + q, k''; k' + q, k')\right\}. \quad (8.11)$$

This equation can be solved by summing over all values of k so that we get a single linear equation. The solution is

$$\sum_k \sum_{k'} G_\nu(k + q, k; k' + q, k') = X(q, \nu)/[1 + (4\pi e^2\beta/\mathcal{U}q^2)X(q, \nu)],$$
$$(8.12)$$

where

$$X(q, \nu) = \frac{1}{2\beta}\sum_k\left\{\frac{\tanh\left[\frac{1}{2}\beta(\epsilon_{k+q} - \mu)\right] - \tanh\left[\frac{1}{2}\beta(\epsilon_k - \mu)\right]}{\epsilon_{k+q} - \epsilon_k - 2\pi i\nu/\beta}\right\}$$
$$= \frac{1}{2\beta}\sum_k \tanh\left[\frac{1}{2}\beta(\epsilon_k - \mu)\right]$$
$$\times \left\{\frac{1}{\epsilon_k - \epsilon_{k-q} - 2\pi i\nu/\beta} - \frac{1}{\epsilon_{k+q} - \epsilon_k - 2\pi i\nu/\beta}\right\}. \quad (8.13)$$

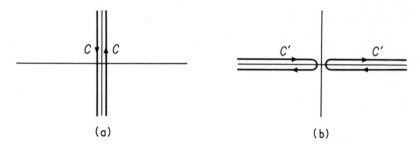

FIG. 27. The two contours used in Eq. (8.15).

Equations (8.8), (8.12) and (8.13) determine the Green's function for imaginary values of the time argument, but we are more interested in its behaviour for real values of this argument. If we define a function $f(q, z)$ by

$$f(q, z) = X(q, \beta z/2\pi i)/[1 + (4\pi e^2 \beta/\mho q^2) X(q, \beta z/2\pi i)],$$

$$X(q, \beta z/2\pi i) = \frac{1}{2\beta} \sum_k \left\{ \frac{\tanh\left[\tfrac{1}{2}\beta(\epsilon_{k+q} - \mu)\right] - \tanh\left[\tfrac{1}{2}\beta(\epsilon_k - \mu)\right]}{\epsilon_{k+q} - \epsilon_k - z} \right\},$$

(8.14)

we can write the Green's function for $0 < u < \beta$ as

$$\sum_k \sum_{k'} G(k + q, k; k' + q, k'; -iu)$$

$$= (2\pi i)^{-1}\beta \int_C f(q, z) \exp(uz)[\exp(\beta z) - 1]^{-1} dz$$

$$= (2\pi i)^{-1}\beta \int_{C'} f(q, z) \exp(uz)[\exp(\beta z) - 1]^{-1} dz, \quad (8.15)$$

where the contours C and C' are the contours shown in Fig. 27. The contour C surrounds the imaginary axis, and the contour C' surrounds the whole of the real axis except for the point zero. The singularities of $[\exp(\beta z) - 1]^{-1}$ are poles on the imaginary axis at $z = 2\pi i\nu/\beta$, where ν is any integer, and all the singularities of $f(z)$ are assumed to be on the real axis. If $f(z)$ has singularities elsewhere, it can be shown that our approximation is inconsistent. Since the Green's function for real positive values of the time argument is an analytic continuation of the function for negative imaginary values (by our definition of the time-ordering process), we can evaluate it by replacing u by it in this equation. For negative values of t, we can use Eqs. (8.7) and (8.15) to get the analytic continuation. The result is

$$\sum_k \sum_{k'} G(k + q, k; k' + q, k'; t)$$

$$= \begin{cases} (\beta/2\pi i) \int_{C'} f(q, z) \exp{(izt)} [1 - \exp{(-\beta z)}]^{-1} dz & \text{for } t < 0, \\ \\ (\beta/2\pi i) \int_{C'} f(q, z) \exp{(izt)} [\exp{(\beta z)} - 1]^{-1} dz & \text{for } t > 0. \end{cases} \tag{8.16}$$

The poles of the function $f(q, z)$ give the excitation energies of those states which are excited by creating one particle and one hole. This can be seen by expressing the Fourier transform of Eq. (8.4) in the energy representation; we get an expression analogous to Eq. (5.63). The equation for a pole of this function is, from Eq. (8.14),

$$1 + \frac{2\pi e^2}{\mathcal{V} q^2} \sum_k \frac{\tanh{\left[\tfrac{1}{2}\beta(\epsilon_{k+q} - \mu)\right]} - \tanh{\left[\tfrac{1}{2}\beta(\epsilon_k - \mu)\right]}}{\epsilon_{k+q} - \epsilon_k - z} = 0, \tag{8.17}$$

which is an equation similar to Eq. (5.78). Like Eq. (5.78), this has almost all of its roots lying in the range of possible values of $\epsilon_{k+q} - \epsilon_k$, but it has two roots right outside this range, one positive and one negative. The excited state to which these roots correspond is known as the *plasma mode*, and the roots are at $\pm \hbar \omega_p(q)$, where $\omega_p(q)$ is the frequency of the plasma mode with wave number q. The plasma frequency can be found by replacing the sum over k in Eq. (8.17) by an integral.

This equation has been studied for a number of special cases. The classical limit (μ large and negative) has been examined by Bohm and Gross (1949), and the zero-temperature limit by Bohm and Pines (1953), Pines (1953), and by Sawada *et al.* (1957). The general expression has been derived by Montroll and Ward (1958). The most important feature of the equation is that the solution has a finite limit as q tends to zero. If we assume that the effective mass approximation is valid, so that we have

$$\epsilon_k = \text{const.} + \hbar^2 k^2 / 2M^* \tag{8.18}$$

in the region of interest, we find that Eq. (8.17) becomes

$$0 = 1 + (2\pi e^2/\mathcal{U}q^2) \sum_k \{1 - \tanh\left[\tfrac{1}{2}\beta(\epsilon_k - \mu)\right]\}$$

$$\times \{[\hbar^2(2\mathbf{k}\cdot\mathbf{q} + q^2)/2M^* - z]^{-1} - [\hbar^2(2\mathbf{k}\cdot\mathbf{q} - q^2)/2M^* - z]^{-1}\}$$

$$= 1 + \frac{2\pi e^2}{\mathcal{U}q^2} \sum_k \{1 - \tanh\left[\tfrac{1}{2}\beta(\epsilon_k - \mu)\right]\} \frac{M^*}{2\hbar^2 kq}$$

$$\times \log \frac{z^2 - \hbar^4(2kq + q^2)^2/4M^{*2}}{z^2 - \hbar^4(2kq - q^2)^2/4M^{*2}}, \qquad (8.19)$$

where we have averaged over all directions of $\mathbf{k}$. We can expand this equation as a power series in q to get the dispersion law for small q. We use the fact that $\tfrac{1}{2}\{1 - \tanh\left[\tfrac{1}{2}\beta(\epsilon_k - \mu)\right]\}$ is the probability of occupation of the level k to get

$$\omega_p^2(q) = 4\pi e^2 n/M^* + \hbar^2 \langle k^2 \rangle q^2/M^{*2}, \qquad (8.20)$$

where $\langle k^2 \rangle$ denotes the average value of k^2 in the unperturbed distribution, and n is the density of electrons. This formula was derived by Bonch-Bruevich and Kogan (1959) in this form.

We can see from Eq. (8.20) that these plasma oscillations have a group velocity that tends to zero as the wave number tends to zero, and so the long wavelength plasma oscillations have a high frequency, but are almost stationary. In the long wavelength limit, an accurate classical description of plasma oscillations is possible. We can treat the plasma as a continuum if the velocity of the electrons is not sufficient for them to travel a significant fraction of a wavelength during the period of the oscillation.

The classical theory of plasma oscillations is due to Langmuir and Tonks (1929). Poisson's equation gives

$$\operatorname{div} \mathcal{E} = -4\pi e \delta n, \qquad (8.21)$$

where $\mathcal{E}$ is the electric field and δn is the excess of negative over positive charge at a point. The continuity equation is

$$\partial n/\partial t + \operatorname{div} \mathbf{j} = 0, \qquad (8.22)$$

where the current density is

$$\mathbf{j} = n\mathbf{v} = (n_0 + \delta n)\,\mathbf{v}, \qquad (8.23)$$

The equation of motion of the electrons is

$$M\left[\frac{\partial \mathbf{v}}{\partial t} + (\mathbf{v}\cdot\operatorname{grad})\mathbf{v}\right] = -e\mathcal{E} \qquad (8.24)$$

where M is the mass of an electron. We treat $\mathbf{v}$ and δn as first order quantities and ignore all second order terms. Substituting Eq. (8.24) in Eq. (8.21) we get

$$M \text{ div } (\partial \mathbf{v}/\partial t) = 4\pi e^2 \delta n \qquad (8.25)$$

Substituting Eq. (8.23) in Eq. (8.22) and differentiating with respect to time we get

$$\frac{\partial^2 (\delta n)}{\partial t^2} + n_0 \text{ div } \frac{\partial \mathbf{v}}{dt} = 0, \qquad (8.26)$$

so that we can combine Eqs. (8.26) and (8.25) to get

$$\frac{\partial^2 (\delta n)}{\partial t^2} + \frac{4\pi e^2 n_0}{M} \delta n = 0. \qquad (8.27)$$

This equation shows that the electron density oscillates about its equilibrium distribution with a frequency

$$\omega_p = \sqrt{4\pi e^2 n_0 / M}. \qquad (8.28)$$

The frequency does not depend at all on the form of the deviation of the density from its equilibrium value, in this approximation; a plasma oscillation is therefore a wave with infinite phase velocity and zero group velocity.

4. Correlation energy

A direct calculation of the energy of an electron gas at zero temperature, or of the pressure at finite temperatures, by means of perturbation theory is not possible, since some of the terms in the series are infinite. Consider the situation at zero temperature, for which the graphs of lowest order are shown in Figs. 5 and 6. Figure 5(a) represents the direct Coulomb interaction between the electrons, which gives an infinite energy, but which would be exactly cancelled by the interaction of the electrons with a uniform background of positive charge neutralizing the electron charge. The positive charge in a metal or in a plasma is not uniformly distributed, but corrections due to this are not very difficult to evaluate. Figure 5(b) represents the *exchange energy* of the degenerate system. Since the contribution of such a graph is inversely proportional to the difference in momentum of the two interacting particles, the exchange energy per unit volume is proportional to $e^2 n^{4/3}$, where n is the density of electrons. The terms proportional to e^4 are given by the graphs shown in Fig. 6, since, substituting the Coulomb potential in the right hand side of Eq. (4.36), we have

$$W_2 = \frac{1}{2\upsilon^2} \sum_q \left\{ \sum_{\substack{l < k_F \\ |1+\mathbf{q}| > k_F}} \sum_{\substack{l' < k_F \\ |1'-\mathbf{q}| > k_F}} \frac{2M^*/\hbar^2}{l^2 + l'^2 - (1+\mathbf{q})^2 - (1'-\mathbf{q})^2} \right.$$
$$\left. \times \frac{4\pi e^2}{q^2} \left[\frac{4\pi e^2}{q^2} - \frac{4\pi e^2}{(1 - 1' + \mathbf{q})^2} \right] \right\}. \quad (8.29)$$

As the momentum transfer $\hbar q$ approaches zero, the number of values of l which satisfy the conditions $l < k_F$, $|1 + \mathbf{q}| > k_F$, tends to zero proportionally to q, as does the number of values of l' which satisfy the conditions on l'. For small q, the expression inside the curly brackets is therefore proportional to q^{-3}, and the sum diverges logarithmically as a result.

The difference between the actual energy of the electron gas and the sum of the kinetic and exchange energies is known as the *correlation energy*. The correlation energy is certainly negative, since the kinetic energy and exchange energy together give the expectation value of the Hamiltonian for a determinant of plane waves, and the actual energy must be lower. The earliest attempt to estimate it was made by Wigner (1934), who used a trial wave function that allows for correlation between particles of opposite spin to estimate the correlation energy. Wigner's method is essentially a high density method, but it is obvious that at low densities the stable configuration must be one in which the electrons form a lattice. The energy of electrons in such a lattice can be calculated, so interpolation between the high and low density results is possible.

A similar problem arises if we wish to calculate the pressure at finite temperatures, since the perturbation series also has infinite terms, and we shall consider this more general problem. The idea of using perturbation theory to evaluate the correlation energy was proposed by Gell-Mann and Brueckner (1957), who observed that the graphs which have the highest divergence in each order of perturbation theory are the ones shown in Fig. 28. These graphs can be formally summed for

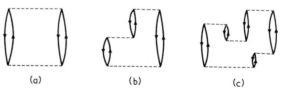

(a)   (b)   (c)

FIG. 28. The graphs in second, third and fifth orders of perturbation theory that are most divergent for a Coulomb interaction.

fixed momentum transfer $\mathbf{q}$, and give an expression that is integrable for small q, although the terms in the expansion are themselves not integrable. It was shown by Montroll and Ward (1958) that graphs like those of Fig. 28 are the most important ones both for very high density and low temperature, and for high temperature and low density. In the former case they give the results of Gell-Mann and Brueckner (1957), and in the latter case they lead to the theory of Debye and Hückel (1923), originally developed to treat correlation in an ionic solution. It is clear that perturbation theory cannot lead to the correct results at low density and low temperature, since the energy density of the lattice that is formed must, from dimensional arguments, be proportional to $e^2 n^{4/3}$. The only term in perturbation theory that can contribute to an expression of this form is the exchange energy, and this leads to the wrong coefficient for the term.

We can express the sum of the graphs shown in Fig. 28 in terms of the Green's function by using a trick suggested by Kinoshita and Nambu (1954). If we break one of the graphs by removing one interaction, we get a graph that contributes to the Green's function. For example, we can break Fig. 28(b) in one of three different places, and we get the three graphs shown in Fig. 29. There is, in fact, a general relation between the Green's function and the pressure which we can exploit. If the potential is made proportional to some coupling constant g, then the derivative of $\log Z$ with respect to g is $-\beta$ times the expectation value of the potential energy, as is clear from Eqs. (6.5) and (6.6). The expectation value of the potential energy is, from Eq. (8.4),

$$\langle V \rangle = -\kappa T g \frac{d \log Z(g)}{dg}$$

$$= \tfrac{1}{2} \lim_{u \to +0} \sum_{k_1} \sum_{k_2} \sum_{k_3} \sum_{k_4} V_{k_1 k_3, k_2 k_4} [G(k_2, k_1; k_3, k_4; -iu)$$

$$- \delta_{k_1 k_4} \delta_{k_2 k_3} S_{k_2}(0)], \quad (8.30)$$

where the Green's function depends on the coupling constant g. To obtain the actual value of $\log Z$, we must integrate this expression. In our problem, the coupling constant is e^2, and, if we take just the direct

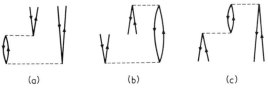

(a)   (b)   (c)

FIG. 29. Graphs obtained by removing one interaction from Fig. 28(b).

part of the potential, we can use Eq. (8.12) to evaluate Eq. (8.30). The terms which involve the one-particle Green's functions S contribute only to the first order term in log Z, so, if we neglect such terms, we make an error that can be corrected later by using the known first order term in log Z. If we neglect these terms, it does not matter whether we let u tend to zero from above or below, and we get

$$-\kappa T \frac{d \log Z(e^2)}{de^2} = \tfrac{1}{2} \lim_{u \to 0} \sum_{q \neq 0} \sum_k \sum_{k'} \frac{4\pi}{\mho q^2} G(k + q, k; k' + q, k'; -iu)$$

$$= \tfrac{1}{2} \sum_\nu \sum_{q \neq 0} \frac{4\pi}{\mho q^2} \frac{X(q, \nu)}{1 + (4\pi e^2 \beta / \mho q^2) X(q, \nu)}. \qquad (8.31)$$

This can be integrated immediately, and gives

$$\log (Z/Z_0) = -\tfrac{1}{2} \sum_\nu \sum_{q \neq 0} \log [1 + (4\pi e^2 \beta / \mho q^2) X(q, \nu)]. \qquad (8.32)$$

This does not give the first order term, the exchange energy, correctly, but the difference between this expression and the first order term in its expansion in powers of e^2 does give the sum of the graphs shown in Fig. 28. The contribution to $-p\mho$ of the correlation between electrons is, in this approximation,

$$-(p\mho)_{\text{corr.}} = \tfrac{1}{2} \kappa T \sum_\nu \sum_{q \neq 0} \left\{ \log \left[1 + \frac{4\pi e^2}{\kappa T \mho q^2} X(q, \nu) \right] - \frac{4\pi e^2}{\kappa T \mho q^2} X(q, \nu) \right\},$$

and this is the expression that becomes equal to the correlation energy in the zero-temperature limit.

The method of evaluating this expression depends on the physical situation. At very high temperatures, β is small, and so it is apparent from Eq. (8.13) that the term with $\nu = 0$ must be the most important one. We have, from Eq. (8.13),

$$X(q, 0) = \frac{M^* \kappa T}{\hbar^2 q} \sum_k \frac{f_k}{k} \log \left| \frac{2k + q}{2k - q} \right|$$

$$\approx M^* \kappa T \sum_k f_k (\hbar k)^{-2}, \qquad (8.34)$$

if q is much less than the mean value of k. This expression is equal to the total number of particles in the Maxwell-Boltzmann distribution, and to $3M^* \kappa T / \hbar^2 k_F^2$ times the number of particles in a degenerate Fermi-Dirac distribution. The condition for this approximation to be good is

$$\frac{e^2 \hbar^2 n}{M^* (\kappa T)^2} \ll 1, \qquad (8.35)$$

or that the product of the potential energy per particle, which goes like $e^2n^{1/3}$, and the zero-point energy, proportional to $\hbar^2n^{2/3}/M^*$, should be much less than the square of the thermal energy This is clearly not a sufficient condition, since we know that a lattice is formed if the potential energy is greater than the thermal energy, however small the zero-point energy is. It is possible for the condition (8.35) to be satisfied for a degenerate Fermi gas, with κT less than the zero-point energy, but this could only happen at very high densities, much higher than the density of electrons in a metal. If we put $X(q, 0) = n\mathbb{U}$, the result given by Eq. (8.34) for a Maxwell-Boltzmann distribution, in Eq. (8.33), we get the correction to the pressure as

$$- p_{\text{corr.}} = (\kappa T/4\pi)\int_0^\infty \{\log(1 + 4\pi e^2\beta n/q^2) - 4\pi e^2\beta n/q^2\}q^2 dq$$

$$= -\tfrac{2}{3}\sqrt{\pi}e^3n^{3/2}(\kappa T)^{-1/2}. \tag{8.36}$$

This is the Debye-Hückel correction to the pressure, which should be good at high temperatures. At very high densities and temperatures, where the inequality (8.35) holds although the system is degenerate, the correction to the pressure is equal to the sum of the exchange effect and the correlation effect, so that we have

$$-p_{\text{exch.}} - p_{\text{corr.}} = -\frac{3e^2nk_F}{4\pi} - \frac{2}{\pi\sqrt{3\pi}}\frac{e^2n^{1/2}(\kappa T)M^{*3/2}}{\hbar^3}. \tag{8.37}$$

The exchange correction should be much more important than the correlation correction, according to Eq. (8.35). It is necessary to remember that n in these formulae stands for the unperturbed density of particles, and calculations of the corrections to the energy, density, and specific heat should be made by expressing n as a function of the temperature and chemical potential.

At very low temperatures, $X(q, \nu)$ does not change rapidly as ν varies, and so we have to evaluate the sum over ν. For small q, the value of $X(q, \nu)$ is, from Eq. (8.13),

$$X(q, \nu) = \frac{M^*}{2\hbar^2\beta q}\sum_k\frac{f_k}{k}\log\frac{\hbar^4(2kq + q^2)^2/4M^{*2} + 4\pi^2\nu^2/\beta^2}{\hbar^4(2kq - q^2)^2/4M^{*2} + 4\pi^2\nu^2/\beta^2}$$

$$\approx \frac{\hbar^2q^2}{\beta M^*}\sum_k f_k \bigg/ \left(\frac{\hbar^4k^2q^2}{M^{*2}} + \frac{4\pi^2\nu^2}{\beta^2}\right)$$

$$= \frac{M^*n\mathbb{U}}{3\beta\hbar^2k_F{}^2}\left(1 - \frac{2\pi\nu M^*}{\beta\hbar^2k_Fq}\tan^{-1}\frac{\beta\hbar^2k_Fq}{2\pi\nu M^*}\right). \tag{8.38}$$

We can substitute this expression in Eq. (8.33) for small q and replace the sum over ν by an integral. If we were to make this substitution for all values of q, we should get a divergent integral, so we make this substitution for q less than αk_F, where α is some small number, and for q greater than αk_F we use the power series expansion. We get in this way

$$-p_{\text{corr.}} \approx \frac{1}{4\pi^2}\int_{-\infty}^{\infty}dx\int_0^{\alpha k_F} q^2 dq \left\{ \log\left[1 + \frac{4\pi e^2 M^* n}{3\hbar^2 k_F^2 q^2} \right.\right.$$

$$\times \left.\left(1 - \frac{2\pi x M^*}{\hbar^2 k_F q}\tan^{-1}\frac{\hbar^2 k_F q}{2\pi x M^*} \right)\right] - \frac{4\pi e^2 M^* n}{3\hbar^2 k_F^2 q^2}\left(1 - \frac{2\pi x M^*}{\hbar^2 k_F q}\tan^{-1}\frac{\hbar^2 k_F q}{2\pi x M^*} \right)\right\}$$

$$- \frac{1}{8\pi^2}\int_{-\infty}^{\infty}dx\int_{\alpha k_F}^{\infty} q^2 dq \left[\frac{4\pi e^2 \beta}{\mathcal{U} q^2}X(q,\beta x) \right]^2. \quad (8.39)$$

This is an expression for the pressure if it is regarded as a function of the chemical potential, and for the correlation energy if it is regarded as a function of the density. The second of these two integrals is finite, since Eq. (8.38) shows that $X(q, \beta x)$ is proportional to

$$q^2/(\hbar^4 q^4/4M^{*2} + 4\pi^2 x^2)$$

for large q, and it contributes a term proportional to $e^4 M^* n/\hbar^2$ to the pressure. The integrand of the first integral is proportional to q^{-1} for large q, and so the integral is proportional to

$$(e^4 M^* n/\hbar^2)\ \log\ (e^2 M^*/\hbar^2 k_F)$$

for large k_F. There is another term proportional to $e^4 M^* n/\hbar^2$ which comes from the exchange terms shown in Figs. 6(c) and (d). The coefficients of these terms were calculated by Gell-Mann and Brueckner (1957). It has, however, been shown by Ferrell (1958) that this approximation is not adequate at metallic densities, since there is a general theorem which implies that the second derivative of the energy with respect to e^2 must be negative. The second derivative of the expression obtained by Gell-Mann and Brueckner changes sign, and so the theory can only be applicable at densities above the actual densities of electrons in metals. Ferrell's criticism does not apply to the original expression (8.33), whose second derivative with respect to e^2 must certainly be negative. A further study of other terms in the high density expansion of the energy of an electron gas has been made by DuBois (1959). The contribution of these terms to the low temperature specific heat of a high density electron gas has been calculated by Gell-Mann (1957).

It is instructive to rewrite Eq. (8.33) as a contour integral. We have

$$
- (p\mathcal{V})_{\text{corr.}} = \frac{1}{4\pi i} \lim_{u \to +0} \sum_q \int_C \left\{ \log \left[1 + \frac{4\pi e^2 \beta}{\mathcal{V} q^2} X(q, \beta z/2\pi i) \right] \right.
$$

$$
\left. - \frac{4\pi e^2 \beta}{\mathcal{V} q^2} X(q, \beta z/2\pi i) \right\} e^{uz} (e^{\beta z} - 1)^{-1} dz
$$

$$
= \frac{1}{4\pi i} \sum_q \int_{C'} \left\{ \log \left[1 + \frac{4\pi e^2 \beta}{\mathcal{V} q^2} X(q, \beta z/2\pi i) \right] \right.
$$

$$
\left. - \frac{4\pi e^2 \beta}{\mathcal{V} q^2} X(q, \beta z/2\pi i) \right\} (e^{\beta z} - 1)^{-1} dz. \quad (8.40)
$$

where C and C' are the contours shown in Fig. 27. We can use the fact that X, as defined by Eq. (8.14), is an even function of z to write this as an integral round a contour C'' which surrounds only the positive real axis. Integration of Eq. (8.40) by parts gives

$$
- (p\mathcal{V})_{\text{corr.}} = \frac{1}{4\pi i} \sum_q \int_{C''} \left\{ \left(\frac{4\pi e^2 \beta}{\mathcal{V} q^2} \right)^2 X(q, \beta z/2\pi i) \frac{\partial x(q, \beta z/2\pi i)}{\partial z} \right.
$$

$$
\times \left[1 + \frac{4\pi e^2 \beta}{\mathcal{V} q^2} X(q, \beta z/2\pi i) \right]^{-1} \right\} \{ -z + 2\beta^{-1} \log (e^{\beta z} - 1) \} dz. \quad (8.41)
$$

The expression in the first set of curly brackets on the right hand side of this equation is a function that has a simple pole of residue minus one at each root of Eq. (8.17), and a second-order pole with residue plus one at each pole of X. The expression in the second set of curly brackets is regular on the positive real axis, so the integral reduces to a sum of terms like

$$
\pm \{ \tfrac{1}{2} z_0 - \beta^{-1} \log (e^{\beta z_0} - 1) \} = \pm \{ -\beta^{-1} \log [2 \sinh (\tfrac{1}{2} \beta z_0)] \}, \quad (8.42)
$$

where there is a plus sign if z_0 is a root of Eq. (8.17), and a minus sign if z_0 is a pole of X. A pole of $X(q, \beta z/2\pi i)$ occurs, as is clear from Eq. (8.14), at each possible value of $\epsilon_{k+q} - \epsilon_k$, and so these poles give the uncoupled particle-hole excitation energies. The roots of Eq. (8.17) are the poles of the Green's functions, and so they give the coupled particle-hole excitation energies. The expression (8.42) is just the contribution to the pressure of a boson mode of energy z_0, as can be seen by comparing it with Eq. (6.11a), and it reduces to the zero-point energy as the temperature tends to zero. Our expression for the correction to the pressure due to correlations is therefore equal to the difference between the contributions of the coupled and the uncoupled boson-like excitations to the pressure. A discussion of the correlation energy of an electron gas along these lines has been given in the papers by Sawada (1957), Brout (1957), and Sawada *et al.* (1957).

5. Screening

Screening is a third phenomenon very closely related to the theory of plasma oscillations and the theory of correlation energy. We can calculate the screening of the electrostatic field due to a charge embedded in the medium by using perturbation theory. To do this, we calculate the change in thermodynamic potential when charges e_1 and e_2 are placed at $\mathbf{r}_1$ and $\mathbf{r}_2$ in the medium, while the temperature and chemical potential are kept constant. The derivative of this with respect to $\mathbf{r}_1$ or $\mathbf{r}_2$ gives the force acting on the particles, and so it gives the electrostatic field. Since the medium is electrically neutral, there is no term linear in e_1 or e_2. There may be terms proportional to $e_1{}^2$ and $e_2{}^2$, but these must be independent of $\mathbf{r}_1$ and $\mathbf{r}_2$ if the medium is uniform, and they contribute to the self-energy of the charges. The terms we are interested in are proportional to $e_1 e_2$.

We regard the medium as the unperturbed system, so that the perturbing Hamiltonian is

$$H_1 = -\int e\rho(\mathbf{r})\left(\frac{e_1}{|\mathbf{r} - \mathbf{r}_1|} + \frac{e_2}{|\mathbf{r} - \mathbf{r}_2|}\right) d^3\mathbf{r}, \quad (8.43)$$

where $\rho(\mathbf{r})$ is the density operator for electrons in the medium. This does not include the interaction of the charges with one another or with the static positive background. Substitution of this in Eqs. (7.2) and (6.6) gives the change in thermodynamic potential as

$$-\delta p\mathcal{V} = \frac{e_1 e_2}{|r_1 - r_2|} - \tfrac{1}{2}\int d^3\mathbf{r}\int d^3\mathbf{r}'\int_0^\beta du \frac{e^2 e_1 e_2}{|\mathbf{r} - \mathbf{r}_1||\mathbf{r}' - \mathbf{r}_2|}$$
$$\times \left(\langle \rho(\mathbf{r}, -iu)\rho(\mathbf{r}', 0)\rangle + \langle \rho(\mathbf{r}', -iu)\rho(\mathbf{r}, 0)\rangle\right). \quad (8.44)$$

The first term on the right hand side comes from the direct interaction of the charges with one another, and the other term is the term proportional to $e_1 e_2$ that results from the interaction of the charges with the medium. The expectation values of products of time-dependent density operators are given by the Green's function defined in Eq. (8.4), since the density operator is

$$\rho(\mathbf{r}) = \sum_k \sum_q a_k{}^\dagger a_{k+q} \exp(i\mathbf{q}\cdot\mathbf{r}). \quad (8.45)$$

Because we integrate over u from 0 to β, only the $\nu = 0$ component of the Fourier expansion (8.8) is left, and the change in the thermo-dynamic potential is

$$-\mho\delta p = \frac{2e_1 e_2}{\pi|\mathbf{r}_1 - \mathbf{r}_2|}\int_0^\infty \frac{\sin(q|\mathbf{r}_1 - \mathbf{r}_2|)}{q}$$

$$\times\left[1 - \frac{4\pi e^2\beta}{\mho q^2}\sum_k\sum_{k'}G_0(k+q, k; k'+q, k')\right]dq. \quad (8.46)$$

This gives the screening in terms of the zero component of the Green's function and is exact if e_1 and e_2 are small enough. The expression is derived by Bonch-Bruevich and Kogan (1959). We can use the approximate expression for G_0 given by Eq. (8.12) to get

$$-\mho\delta p = \frac{2e_1 e_2}{\pi|\mathbf{r}_1 - \mathbf{r}_2|}\int_0^\infty \frac{\sin(q|\mathbf{r}_1 - \mathbf{r}_2|)}{q} \frac{1}{1 + (4\pi e^2\beta/\mho q^2)X(q, 0)}dq.$$

$$(8.47)$$

For very small q, X tends to the value given by Eq. (8.34). For very large values of $|r_1 - r_2|$, the thermodynamic potential is therefore

$$-\mho\delta p = \frac{e_1 e_2}{|\mathbf{r}_1 - \mathbf{r}_2|}\exp\left(-\frac{|\mathbf{r}_1 - \mathbf{r}_2|}{r_0}\right), \quad (8.48)$$

where the screening length r_0 is given by

$$r_0 = \sqrt{\kappa T/4\pi n e^2} \quad (8.49a)$$

in the classical case, and by

$$r_0 = \sqrt{k_F^2/12\pi n M^* e^2} \quad (8.49b)$$

for a degenerate Fermi gas.

These results can be obtained in an elementary way if we assume that the effect of electron interactions can be described by the interaction of each electron with a local field due to all the other electrons. With this assumption we can calculate the field due to a charge e_1 at the origin. In the case of a degenerate Fermi gas, this approximation leads to the Thomas-Fermi theory which was discussed in Chapter III. In the classical case, the condition that the chemical potential should be constant leads to the density of electrons

$$\rho(r) = \rho_0 \exp[e\varphi(r)/\kappa T], \quad (8.50a)$$

where $\varphi(r)$ is the local electrostatic potential, and ρ_0 is the density of electrons a long way from the origin, equal to the density of positive charge. For the degenerate Fermi gas we have

$$\rho(r) = (2M)^{3/2}[\mu + e\varphi(r)]^{3/2}/3\pi^2,$$

$$\rho_0 = (2M)^{3/2}\mu^{3/2}/3\pi^2. \tag{8.50b}$$

We now use Poisson's equation, and expand the right hand sides in powers of $\varphi(r)$, keeping only the leading term, since we assume that the charge e_1 is very small. In the classical case this gives

$$\begin{aligned}
\nabla^2\varphi(r) &= 4\pi e[\rho(r) - \rho_0] \\
&= 4\pi e\rho_0 \{\exp[e\varphi(r)/\kappa T] - 1\} \\
&\approx (4\pi e^2\rho_0/\kappa T)\varphi(r), \tag{8.51a}
\end{aligned}$$

which is the expression obtained by Debye and Hückel (1923) while for the degenerate Fermi gas it gives

$$\begin{aligned}
\nabla^2\varphi(r) &= 4\pi e(2M)^{3/2}\{[\mu + e\varphi(r)]^{3/2} - \mu^{3/2}\}/3\pi^2 \\
&\approx [4\pi e^2\mu^{1/2}(2M)^{3/2}/2\pi^2]\varphi(r) \\
&= (12\pi e^2\rho_0 M/k_F{}^2)\varphi(r). \tag{8.51b}
\end{aligned}$$

These two equations have solutions of the form

$$\varphi(r) = (e_1/r)\exp(-r/r_0), \tag{8.52}$$

where the screening lengths r_0 are given by Eqs. (8.49a) and (8.49b) in the two cases.

6. Survey of alternative techniques

A large number of apparently different techniques have been used to derive the results discussed in this chapter and in Chapter V. Since the results obtained are always the same, it is clear that the approximations used in the various methods must be closely related, although the relations are not always obvious. It is useful to survey some of the other methods that have been used, since such a survey may help to show what are the physical assumptions that lead to the approximations. In Chapter V, Sec. 10, we have discussed one alternative approach based on the time-dependent Hartree-Fock equations. The original method of Bohm and Pines (1953) was to try to make a canonical transformation which would separate out collective variables (plasmon coordinates in the case of the electron gas). It was emphasized by Tomonaga (1955b) that the separation is only approximate, but that the errors seem to be proportional to N^{-1}, where N is the total number of particles. We discussed this in another context when we considered Eq. (5.55).

The method of Sawada (1957) is very similar to this, although he uses the notation of second quantization. Sawada's argument is that the condition for an operator Q to generate a stationary state of energy E_1 from the ground state $|\Psi_0\rangle$ is that

$$[H, Q]|\Psi_0\rangle = (E_1 - E_0)Q|\Psi_0\rangle \tag{8.53}$$

The simplest operator which can generate a state of momentum $\hbar q$ is

$$Q = \sum_k h_k a_k{}^\dagger a_{k-q}, \tag{8.54}$$

where h_k is some numerical coefficient. If the Hamiltonian is

$$\sum_k (\hbar^2 k^2/2M) a_k{}^\dagger a_k + \tfrac{1}{2}\sum_k \sum_{k'} \sum_{q'} V(q') a_k{}^\dagger a_{k'}{}^\dagger a_{k'+q'} a_{k-q'}, \tag{8.55}$$

the commutator is

$$[H, Q] = \sum_k [\hbar^2 k^2/2M - \hbar^2(\mathbf{k} - \mathbf{q})^2/2M] h_k a_k{}^\dagger a_{k-q}$$

$$+ \tfrac{1}{2}\sum_k \sum_{k'} \sum_{q'} V(q') h_k [a_{k+q'}{}^\dagger a_{k'}{}^\dagger a_{k'+q'} a_{k-q} + a_k{}^\dagger a_{k-q'}{}^\dagger a_{k-q} a_{k'-q'}$$

$$+ a_k{}^\dagger a_{k'}{}^\dagger a_{k'+q'} a_{k-q-q'} + a_{k'}{}^\dagger a_k{}^\dagger a_{k-q+q'} a_{k'-q'}]. \tag{8.56}$$

The argument is that most of the terms which come from the potential energy operator will give a small effect when they operate on the ground state, because their effects are incoherent. However, a combination like $a_k{}^\dagger a_k$ has zero phase, and so must be regarded as particularly important. For this reason, the method is known as the random phase approximation. We keep only the coherent terms in the commutator and get

$$[H, Q] = \sum_k h_k \{\hbar^2 k^2/2M - \hbar^2(k - q)^2/2M$$

$$- \sum_{q'} V(q')(n_{k+q'} - n_{k-q-q'})\} a_k{}^\dagger a_{k-q}$$

$$+ \sum_k \sum_{k'} [V(q) - V(k' - k)] h_k (n_{k-q} - n_k) a_{k'}{}^\dagger a_{k'-q}. \tag{8.57}$$

We can take the number operators n_k to have the values which they have in the unperturbed system (at zero or finite temperature), and then find the condition that the right hand side should be proportional to Q. The random phase approximation gives exactly the same result as the method we have used. The neglect of products of operators which are not coherent is just the same as the neglect of graphs which have not the structure shown in Fig. 28.

A method very similar to the Green's function method we have used here has been proposed by Hubbard (1957). Hubbard regards the interaction as being carried by a virtual boson (in field theory the Coulomb interaction is indeed carried by a longitudinal photon), and considers how the medium modifies the properties of such a boson. A single loop of fermion lines is the simplest boson self-energy part, and this is taken into account in the first approximation. The graphs of Fig. 28 and 29 contain only such boson self-energy parts. This method enables the exchange part of the interaction to be taken into account in a simple manner (Hubbard, 1958).

Recently, several papers have been written to show that these results can be obtained without the use of perturbation theory. A brief discussion has been given by Chen (1959), and the paper of Martin and Schwinger (1959) gives a detailed treatment of the problem. The method is to write differential equations for the time-dependent Green's functions. If there is a two-body potential acting between the particles, the derivative of an n-particle Green's function is given by a sum of n- and $(n + 1)$-particle Green's functions. For example, at zero temperature and for t greater than zero, differentiation of Eq. (5.3) gives

$$- iS_k{}'(t) = \langle \Psi_0 | a_k{}^\dagger \exp\left[-i(H - E_0)t\right][H, a_k]|\Psi_0\rangle$$

$$= T_k S_k(t) + \tfrac{1}{2}\sum_{k'}\sum_{k''}\sum_{k'''}(V_{kk',k''k'''} - V_{kk',k'''k''})$$

$$\times \langle \Psi_0 | a_k{}^\dagger \exp\left[-i(H - E_0)t\right]a_{k'}{}^\dagger a_{k''} a_{k'''}|\Psi_0\rangle. \quad (8.58)$$

There is a similar equation for the derivative of the Green's functions at finite temperatures defined by Eq. (8.1). The approximation used to solve these equations, which form an infinite set of coupled differential equations, is to assume that all Green's functions above a certain order, say n_0, can be expressed as antisymmetrized products of Green's functions of lower order. This is to assume that all graphs with a large number of external lines can be separated into parts connected by no internal line, so that each part has not more than $2n_0$ external lines. If we take $n_0 = 1$, we have to write the Green's function on the right of Eq. (8.58) as the product of one-particle Green's functions, so that we get

$$-iS_k{}'(t) = T_k S_k(t) + \sum_{k'}(V_{kk',kk'} - V_{kk',k'k})\langle \Psi_0 | n_{k'} |\Psi_0\rangle S_k(t). \quad (8.59)$$

This equation shows that the Green's function depends exponentially on time. The amplitude must be

$$\lim_{t \to +0} S_k(t) = \langle \Psi_0 | n_k |\Psi_0\rangle, \quad (8.60)$$

so that the equation for the exponent is coupled only to the *amplitudes* of the other Green's functions. There are very many possible solutions to the equations (8.59) and (8.60) and the equation for $S_k(t)$ with $t < 0$, but most of these solutions do not have the property

$$- S_k[t(1 - i\delta)] \leq \exp(\mu' t \delta), \quad \text{for} \quad t > 0,$$

$$S_k[t(1 + i\delta)] \leq \exp(\mu t \delta), \quad \text{for} \quad t < 0, \qquad (8.61)$$

where δ is a real positive number, and μ and μ' are the chemical potentials for $N - 1$ and N particles. This extra condition shows that all the occupation numbers $\langle \Psi_0 | n_k | \Psi_0 \rangle$ must be zero or unity, and so Eq. (8.59) gives the usual Hartree-Fock expression for the propagator.

The method is not quite clear-cut, since the solution of the truncated system of equations depends on the representation used. It certainly can be made to reproduce most existing theories, and it has been applied successfully to the theory of superconductivity by Kadanoff and Martin (1960).

7. Electrical conductivity

In Chapter V, Sec. 4, we discussed how the single-particle Green's function could describe the decay of a one-particle excited state. Essentially, the lifetime of the excited state is the reciprocal of the width of the peak of the Fourier transform of the time-dependent propagator. In the same way, we expect that the two-particle Green's functions should give information about the lifetimes of the two-particle and particle-hole excited states. It is such lifetimes that determine, to lowest order, the dissipation of energy of an external perturbation. It should therefore be possible to obtain values for the rates of relaxation processes from the two-particle Green's functions, and we might hope to be able to get expressions for the coefficient of viscosity or thermal conductivity of a system.

It has been rigorously demonstrated by Kubo (1956) that the electrical conductivity can be obtained from such a Green's function. Here we give a different derivation, which is very similar to the argument by which we obtained the expression for the screened potential in terms of the Green's function, in Eq. (8.46). At time zero we switch on an electrostatic field which varies sinusoidally in space and time with frequency ω, damping γ, and wave number $\mathbf{q}$. Written as an operator in the interaction picture, the perturbation is

$$H_1(t) = -Ae \exp(iH_0 t) \int [\rho(r) - \rho_0] \sin(\mathbf{q} \cdot \mathbf{r}) d^3\mathbf{r}$$

$$\times \exp(-iH_0 t) \sin(\omega t) \exp(-\gamma t), \qquad (8.62)$$

where H_0 is the Hamiltonian of the system with no external field acting. The expectation value of the energy at time t is

$$\bar{E} = \langle U^\dagger(t)[H_0 + H_1(t)]U(t)\rangle, \qquad (8.63)$$

where $U(t)$ is the development operator in the interaction picture, which satisfies the equations

$$idU(t)/dt = H_1(t)U(t),$$
$$U(0) = 1. \qquad (8.64)$$

To find the total energy that the system takes up, we must evaluate Eq. (8.63) at infinite time, using the expansion (4.13) for $U(t)$. The zero-order term gives the initial energy, the first order term vanishes because the average electron density is equal to the density ρ_0 of positive charge, and the second-order term gives

$$\Delta \bar{E} = \int_0^\infty \int_0^\infty \langle H_1(t)[H_0, H_1(t')]\rangle \, dt dt'. \qquad (8.65)$$

The only operators which come into H_1 are ρ_q and ρ_{-q}, the Fourier components of the density operator. Equation (8.45) shows that the average value is given by the Green's function defined in Eq. (8.4). If the Fourier expansion is

$$\langle [\rho_q(t) - \rho_{-q}(t)][\rho_{-q}(t') - \rho_q(t')]\rangle = \int_{-\infty}^\infty g_q(x)e^{ix(t-t')}dx, \qquad (8.66)$$

where $g_q(x)$ is the real strength function, similar to the strength function defined by Eq. (5.21), then the evaluation of Eq. (8.65) leads to

$$\lim_{\gamma \to 0} \gamma \Delta \bar{E} = \tfrac{1}{16}\pi A^2 e^2 [\omega g_q(\omega) - \omega g_q(-\omega)]. \qquad (8.67)$$

In this problem it is not generally possible to assume momentum conservation, since it is generally processes that do not conserve momentum which give rise to electrical resistance; the ions take up momentum from the electrons in thermal scattering and impurity scattering of the electrons. As a result, we cannot assume that the expectation value of $\rho_q{}^2$ is zero, as it is for an electron gas.

If the conductivity of the material is $\sigma(q, \omega)$, the energy given to the system by the applied potential described by Eq. (8.62) can be calculated as an integral over space and time of the scalar product of the current density and the electrostatic field. This gives

$$\lim_{\gamma \to 0} \gamma \Delta \bar{E} = \tfrac{1}{8}A^2 \mho \hbar q^2 \sigma(\mathbf{q}, \omega). \qquad (8.68)$$

Comparison of Eqs. (8.67) and (8.68) gives the conductivity as

$$\sigma(\mathbf{q}, \omega) = \tfrac{1}{2}\pi e^2[\omega g_q(\omega) - \omega g_q(-\omega)]/\hbar q^2 \mathcal{V}. \tag{8.69}$$

This method gives only the real part of the conductivity, and other methods must be used to calculate the imaginary part, which gives no dissipation of energy.

8. Collective modes in superconductors

The ideas developed in this chapter can be applied to the theory of superconductivity by taking the type of wave function proposed by Bardeen *et al.* (1957) as a first approximation instead of the determinant of plane waves. This leads to a new type of collective excitation, with the energy of a quantum proportional to its momentum, as has been shown by Anderson (1958) and by Bogoliubov *et al.* (1959). At zero temperature, however, when the long range part of the Coulomb interaction is allowed for, this new collective mode is not found (Anderson, 1958). It appears that the type of correlation implied by the existence of this mode is not compatible with the type of correlation needed to screen the Coulomb interaction. There may be other types of collective modes with excitation energies less than the energy gap. These are discussed in the review by Bardeen and Schrieffer (1960).

The Green's function which must be studied is the one defined by Eq. (5.62), and the important graphs are the ladder graphs shown in Fig. 30. These graphs give a sum which diverges as the temperature approaches the critical temperature from above. This divergence indicates that a collective mode is unstable, and the ground state should be chosen differently below this temperature. Below the cirtical temperature, when the Bardeen, Cooper, and Schrieffer wave function is used as a first approximation, the problem is more complicated, because the unperturbed Hamiltonian, defined by Eqs. (6.42) and (6.36), mixes particles and holes. As a result, the graphs of Fig. 29 and 30 are no longer distinct, but the two classes of graphs must be considered to-

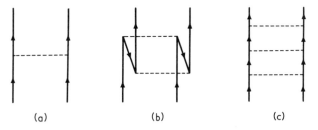

(a)   (b)   (c)

FIG. 30. Ladder graphs.

gether. This is the cause of the interference between Anderson's collective mode and the plasma mode which leads to the disappearance of the former at zero temperature.

In *The Many-Body Problem,* the theory of collective motion is presented by Bohm, and the application of the theory to electrons in a metal is discussed by Pines.

IX. Bosons

1. Introduction

Up to this point we have been almost exclusively concerned with systems of interacting fermions, and we have not discussed interacting bosons at all. Since almost all the methods which can be used for fermions can be used also for bosons, and vice versa, we do not give a detailed discussion of the many-boson problem, but only discuss some of its general features. In some ways, as we shall see, the many-boson problem is simpler than the many-fermion problem. On the other hand, there are fewer physical systems to which the theory can be applied, and so comparison with experiment is even more difficult than it is for the many-fermion theory.

There are two types of system that can be regarded as many-boson systems. In the first type, the particles have a nonzero mass, and the number of bosons is conserved. In the second type of system, the particles have no mass, and the number of bosons is not conserved. The only example of the first type of system is liquid helium. There are of course other liquids composed of bosons, but these are essentially classical fluids and the fact that the molecules obey Bose-Einstein statistics is of no importance. Liquid helium is clearly a quantum liquid, since it is able to remain a liquid at indefinitely low temperatures.

The best-known example of the second type of system is a cavity filled only with electromagnetic radiation in thermal equilibrium with the walls of the cavity. The bosons are photons, and these are essentially noninteracting, at least at temperatures below 10^9 degrees. For this reason, the theory of cavity radiation is simple and well understood, but this cannot be said of other systems of this sort. Another example of a particle which obeys Bose-Einstein statistics is a phonon in a solid. Although a photon can be regarded as a particle in its own right, a phonon cannot be, and it is necessary to take account of the medium

153

which carries the phonons. Phonons interact with one another because the restoring forces on atoms in a crystal are not harmonic. More important, in a metal the phonons interact with the valence electrons, and so we have to consider a system of interacting fermions and bosons.

There are various other examples of this type of system. For phonons in a solid, it does not make any difference whether the atoms of the solid are fermions or bosons; they can usually be regarded as classical particles. Phonon-like excitations can also exist in systems which are predominantly Fermi systems, as we saw when we discussed zero sound and plasma oscillations. They can exist in Bose systems, and we shall see that the low-lying excitations in liquid helium are phonons. They are also very important in ferromagnetic and antiferromagnetic systems, where the important excitations are spin-waves, which behave like bosons. The theories of these different types of excitation are all very similar. In all these cases it is necessary to take account of the interactions of the bosons with the medium, and to allow for the fact that the bosons are not real particles, in order to improve the simplest theories.

2. Liquid helium

The most interesting problem concerning interacting bosons is the problem posed by the superfluidity and related properties of liquid helium. As we mentioned in Chapter VI, there appears to be some relation between the Bose-Einstein condensation of noninteracting bosons and the occurrence of superfluidity, but it is clear that the interactions must be taken into account in some way, since a gas of perfectly noninteracting bosons does not have any of the essential properties of superfluid liquid helium. Since this whole subject has recently been reviewed in a book by Atkins (1959), we give here only an outline of the important features of this problem, and indicate how the theory of interacting bosons is related to the methods we have discussed in connection with the theory of interacting fermions.

The independent particle approximation proved very useful in the many-fermion problem, since a good deal of information can be obtained by studying the Hartree-Fock equations. This approximation is less helpful in the case of interacting bosons. The wave function is a symmetric product of single-particle wave functions, which may all be identical. If the forces are weakly repulsive, the best product wave function is likely to be product of plane waves with momentum zero, since this correlates the particles as little as possible. On the other hand, if the forces are attractive, a lower energy could be obtained by localizing the particles in space. In this way we see that repulsive forces assist condensation in momentum space, the Bose-Einstein condensation, while attractive forces inhibit Bose-Einstein condensation, since they favour condensation in configuration space instead. This argument is presented in detail by Gross (1960c).

To show the effect of the interaction we take a very much simplified soluble model in which we assume that the particles have no kinetic energy (infinite mass), and that they interact only through the diagonal part of a short-range potential. A general local potential is

$$\sum_{q} \sum_{k} \sum_{k'} V(q) b_k{}^\dagger b_{k'}{}^\dagger b_{k'+q} b_{k-q}, \tag{9.1}$$

and, if this has a very short range, $V(q)$ is a constant, equal to $V(0)$. The diagonal part is just

$$\sum_{k} V(0) n_k (n_k - 1) + \sum_{k} \sum_{k' \neq k} [V(\mathbf{k} - \mathbf{k}') + V(0)] n_k n_{k'}$$

$$= 2 \sum_{k} \sum_{k'} V(0) n_k n_{k'} - \sum_{k} V(0) (n_k{}^2 + n_k)$$

$$= (2N^2 - N) V(0) - V(0) \sum_{k} n_k{}^2, \tag{9.2}$$

where n_k is the number operator $b_k{}^\dagger b_k$, and N is the total number of particles. If the potential is attractive, so that $V(0)$ is negative, this expression has a minimum value

$$E_0 = 2(N^2 - N) V(0), \tag{9.3a}$$

which it attains when all the occupation numbers n_k are either one or zero, so there is no Bose-Einstein condensation. This remains true in this model even if the kinetic energy, which favours condensation in momentum space, is taken into consideration. If $V(0)$ is positive, however, Eq. (9.2) has a minimum value

$$E_0 = (N^2 - N) V(0), \tag{9.3b}$$

when one occupation number is N and the others are all zero. The repulsive interaction therefore favours Bose-Einstein condensation.

This model overemphasizes the effect of the repulsive interaction. The lowest excited state, obtained by exciting one particle from the condensate, has an energy E_1 given by

$$E_1 - E_0 = 2(N - 1) V(0), \tag{9.4}$$

and so the model predicts an energy gap independent of the extent of the system, such as is found in the theory of superconductivity. This would explain the occurrence of superfluidity, but it has been shown by

Hugenholtz and Pines (1959) on quite general grounds that the spectrum of liquid helium cannot have an energy gap. Furthermore, the model gives a first order phase transition, whereas a second order transition is observed. Suppose that N_0 particles are condensed in one level, and that f_1B of the remaining B levels are singly occupied, f_2B are doubly occupied, and so on. The number of particles, energy, and entropy are given by

$$N = N_0 + \sum_n nf_n,$$

$$E = V(0)[2N^2 - N - N_0^2 - B\sum_n n^2 f_n],$$

$$S = \kappa \log \frac{B!}{(f_1B)!(f_2B)! \cdots [(1 - f_1 - f_2 - \cdots)B]!}$$

$$\approx \kappa B[-\sum_{n=1} f_n \log f_n - (1 - \sum_{n=1} f_n) \log (1 - \sum_{n=1} f_n)]. \qquad (9.5)$$

Minimizing

$$E - \mu N - TS$$

with respect to the numbers N_0 and f_n, we get

$$(4N - 2N_0)V(0) - \mu = 0,$$

$$-BV(0)n^2 + 4BnNV(0) - \mu Bn + \kappa TB \log [f_n/(1 - \sum_n f_n)] = 0.$$

$$(9.6a)$$

These equations have the solution

$$N = N_0 + B[\exp (2N_0V(0)/\kappa T) - 1]^{-1}. \qquad (9.7)$$

For a given temperature this has a minimum, so that the density of the condensed phase cannot be below a certain value. At lower densities N_0 must be zero, and the normal phase must exist, with a distribution given by

$$4nNV(0) - \mu n + \kappa T \log [f_n/(1 - \sum_n f_n)] = 0. \qquad (9.6b)$$

The transition from the high-density phase to the low-density phase must take place abruptly, so that there is a first order transition, since N_0 cannot go smoothly to zero. Equation (9.7) shows that N_0 can only be zero if the temperature is zero.

The quasiparticle method of Bogoliubov (1947), developed further by Bogoliubov and Zubarev (1955), enables us to understand why a gas of interacting bosons may have superfluid properties; it is not necessary to make the drastic assumptions of the previous two paragraphs in order to get such properties. The method is very similar to the method which we discussed in connection with the theory of superconductivity in Chapter VI, Sec. 7. In the ground state of a Bose gas, a finite fraction of the particles may be in the zero-momentum level, so the creation and annihilation operators referring to this zero-momentum level are treated separately. The other operators are rewritten as quasiparticle operators, by means of an equation similar to Eq. (6.36), apart from a change in sign, and the suppression of the suffix which gives the spin of the electron in Eq. (6.36). These quasiparticle operators are linear combinations of an operator that creates a particle with a certain momentum and an operator that annihilates a particle with the opposite momentum. Just as a suitable choice of the coefficients of the transformation ensures that the state with no quasiparticles has a lower energy than the unperturbed Fermi gas in the superconductivity problem, so also a suitable choice of the coefficients ensures that the state with no quasiparticles of nonzero momentum has a lower energy than the unperturbed Bose gas in this problem, provided that the forces between the bosons are repulsive. More remarkable is the fact that the excitation spectrum, instead of being a quadratic function of momentum as it is for noninteracting bosons, is, for small momentum, a linear function of momentum. It had been shown earlier by Landau (1941) that such an energy spectrum would explain the occurrence of superfluidity, and would be in agreement with the data on the low-temperature specific heat of helium. The ratio of energy to momentum is equal to the velocity of sound, and these low-energy excitations are, in fact, phonons.

The necessity of the quasiparticle transformation becomes obvious when we consider what effect the interactions must have on the state with all particles in the zero-momentum level. Particles in the zero-momentum level can scatter against one another, and to into a pair of levels with opposite momenta. Because of coherence effects, further scattering of the members of an excited pair against one another is more important than the interaction of one pair with another; the ground state is therefore very similar to the ground state in the Bardeen et al. (1957) theory of superconductivity. The quasiparticles are to some extent stabilized by the Bose-Einstein condensation, since the more rapid variation of quasiparticle energy with momentum makes it more difficult for a quasiparticle to decay in the condensed phase than it is in the uncondensed phase. In Chapter VI, Sec. 9, we discussed how the pairing has a similar effect in nuclei and other Fermi systems.

There are several important differences between the two theories.

In the fermion problem, the superfluid state is produced by attractive forces, whereas repulsive forces are needed in the boson problem. In the fermion problem, the excitation spectrum goes down to zero in the independent particle model (Hartree-Fock approximation), but has an energy gap in the quasiparticle model. In the boson problem, there is an energy gap in the independent particle model, and the spectrum goes linearly to zero in the quasiparticle model. In a sense, therefore, the pairing has opposite effects in the two cases. A comparison between the two theories has been made by Valatin and Butler (1958).

The theory of liquid helium has been discussed in a very elegant manner by Feynman (1953, 1954). Feynman exploits some of the simplifying features of the boson problem, and uses several ideas which have not been successfully employed in the fermon problem. The main simplifying feature is that the ground state wave function is real and positive everywhere. This can be proved easily, since, if Ψ is any symmetric wave function, $|\Psi|$ is also a symmetric wave function. Furthermore, the expectation value of the Hamiltonian cannot be more for $|\Psi|$ than it is for Ψ, so that the variational principle shows that the ground state wave function can always be chosen to be real and positive. This fact enables us to use a representation of the wave function that can be easily visualized. We can draw the position of every particle in the system, and call a particular choice of positions a configuration. There are many possible configurations, and a wave function assigns a number to each configuration. In the ground state the number associated with each configuration is always positive, and it must be large if the particles are well separated, but small if any of the particles overlap, so that the strong repulsions between the particles come into operation. An excited state must be orthogonal to the ground state, and so roughly half the configurations must have a positive number associated with them, while the other half have a negative number associated with them. Feynman's argument is that, because of the identity of the particles, it is hard to find a way of defining such excited states which does not use up a considerable amount of kinetic energy. For example, we might have a wave function that is positive if all the particles are at positions shown with solid circles in Fig. 31, and negative when they are at the positions shown with dotted circles, varying smoothly between these two cases. Such a wave function would give a kinetic energy of the order of $\hbar^2/2Mr_0^2$, where r_0 is the mean distance between the particles. One type of excitation which is certainly possible is an oscillation in density. This however is just a sound wave, and its energy is proportional to its momentum.

A quantitative estimate of the energy spectrum can be made by

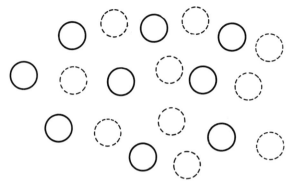

Fig. 31. The solid circles show a typical configuration for which the wave function of an excited state might be positive, and the broken circles a configuration for which the wave function might be negative.

using a variational argument, as was shown in the second paper quoted (Feynman, 1954). If we have an operator Q which gives a state orthogonal to the ground state $|\Psi_0\rangle$ when it operates on $|\Psi_0\rangle$, it is clear that the quantity

$$\frac{\langle\Psi_0|Q^\dagger HQ|\Psi_0\rangle}{\langle\Psi_0|Q^\dagger Q|\Psi_0\rangle} - E_0 = \frac{\langle\Psi_0|Q^\dagger[H,\,Q]|\Psi_0\rangle}{\langle\Psi_0|Q^\dagger Q|\Psi_0\rangle} \qquad (9.8)$$

gives an upper bound for the excitation energy of the first excited state. If Ψ_0 is the wave function for the ground state, a possible trial wave function for an excited state of momentum $\hbar\mathbf{q}$ is

$$\Psi_{\mathbf{q}} = \sum_{j=1}^{N} \exp{(i\mathbf{q}\cdot\mathbf{r}_j)}\Psi_0, \qquad (9.9)$$

where the sum goes over the coordinates r_j of all the particles. This corresponds to taking Q to be a local single-particle operator. With this trial wave function the numerator of Eq. (9.8) can be evaluated immediately, and it is $Nq^2/2M$. The denominator is related to the pair correlation function, which is an experimentally determined quantity. Use of this gives an energy spectrum which lies everywhere above the spectrum deduced from the thermodynamics of liquid helium, but which has the correct general properties. A better form of trial wave function, although more difficult to work with, was proposed by Feynman and Cohen (1956), and this gives results in better agreement with experiment.

Another example of the use of the simple properties of the ground state wave function is given in a paper by Dyson (1957). In this paper Dyson is able to calculate both upper and lower bounds for the energy of a gas of hard-sphere bosons. These bounds are not, however, very close to one another, so the method does not provide a precise answer for the energy.

There have been several calculations of the properties of a system of interacting bosons by use of perturbation theory in one form or another. Since it appears to be the repulsive forces between helium atoms which give rise to the superfluid properties, while attractive forces inhibit the occurrence of superfluidity, attention has been concentrated on the problem of bosons interacting only by means of short-range repulsive forces—hard-sphere bosons. The attractive forces must be responsible for the fact that helium is liquid at all, and some success has been had by Huang (1960) in taking into account the attractive force at intermediate distances as well as the repulsive force between atoms close to one another. The usual problem arises with a hard-sphere gas that the matrix elements of the potential in momentum space are infinite. One way of overcoming this difficulty is by use of the Brueckner theory which we discussed in Chapter IV, Sec. 7. This method was used by Brueckner and Sawada (1957). Another method is to replace the potential by a "pseudo-potential" which has the same scattering properties. This method was developed by Huang and Yang (1957) and applied to the problem of hard-sphere bosons by Lee and associates (1957). Further developments of the pseudopotential method have been made by Abe (1958), so that the method can take account of collisions of more than two particles at once.

The finite temperature perturbation method of Matsubara (1955) is also applicable to bosons, as has been observed in most of the papers on this method (see Chapter VII, Sec. 2, for references). The unperturbed propagators are similar to the unperturbed fermion propagators defined by Eq. (7.10), except that the factors $(1 - f_k)$ and $-f_k$ are replaced by $(N_k + 1)$ and N_k, where N_k is the Bose-Einstein statistical factor $\{\exp [\beta(\epsilon_k - \mu)] - 1\}^{-1}$. This perturbation expansion has been derived in another way by Lee and Yang (1959a), and these authors have used perturbation methods to make a detailed study of the problem of interacting bosons (Lee and Yang, 1959b, 1960).

3. Phonons

The general problem of understanding the effects of the interactions of phonons with one another and with the electrons in a metal is a very complicated problem, and not much progress has been made with it. One difficulty is that the form of the interaction is not easy to determine either theoretically or experimentally, but, apart from this,

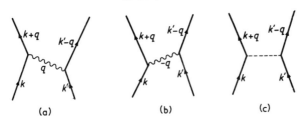

FIG. 32. Graphs showing the exchange of a phonon between two electrons and the equivalent instantaneous interaction.

general methods for dealing with a system of interacting bosons and fermions have not been developed. There are, as a result, only a few special cases in which many-particle methods have had any success.

If we are concerned with electrons of low excitation energy and high density and with phonons of high energy, we can treat the electrons as static particles which exchange phonons, so that there is an effective force between the electrons. This is closely analogous to the meson theory of nuclear forces, in which the effects of the exchange of high energy mesons between low energy nucleons are duplicated by a static nucleon-nucleon potential; we discussed this analogy in Chapter VI, Sec. 5. In perturbation theory language, we replace the graphical elements shown in Figs. 32(a) and (b) by the one shown in Fig. 32(c); the exchange of a phonon, which takes a certain length of time, is replaced by an equivalent instantaneous interaction between the electrons. It does not matter much whether we use finite temperature perturbation theory or ground state perturbation theory, since the occupation probabilities of the high energy phonon levels in which we are interested are very small. If we use the set of rules given in Chapter IV, Sec. 5, we find that the two graphs 32(a) and (b) contribute

$$\frac{[g(q)]^2}{-E - \hbar\omega(q) - \delta} + \frac{[g(q)]^2}{-E - \hbar\omega(q) + \delta}$$

$$= -\frac{[E + \hbar\omega(q)][g(q)]^2}{[E + \hbar\omega(q)]^2 - \delta^2}. \quad (9.10)$$

Here E is the mean energy of the whole graph at the level at which the interaction occurs, $\hbar\omega(q)$ is the phonon energy, $g(q)$ is the phonon-electron matrix element, and δ is the electron energy transferred, given by

$$\delta = \tfrac{1}{2}(\epsilon_k + \epsilon_{k'-q} - \epsilon_{k+q} - \epsilon_{k'}). \quad (9.11)$$

Equation (9.3) gives the effective electron-electron interaction only if the phonon has such high energy that its transfer from one electron to the other occurs so rapidly that no change is likely to take place in the rest of the system while it is in flight; if this condition is not satisfied, E cannot be determined. If the condition is satisfied, the fraction on the right hand side of Eq. (9.3) is positive, and the effective interaction is attractive. The effective interaction does not depend strongly on the energies of the particles involved, unless the electrons are excited by an amount comparable with the phonon energy. This method, due to Fröhlich (1950), justifies the procedure of Bardeen *et al.* (1957) in taking the electron-electron interaction to be a constant if the excitation energy of the electrons is less than the Debye energy, and zero otherwise.

This approximation is only valid if the electron density is high, since rapid exchange of phonons is not otherwise possible. If the electron density is low, the interactions between different valence electrons are unimportant, and only the interaction between one electron and the lattice need be considered. This interaction alters the rest-energy and the effective mass of the electron, and an electron which moves in equilibrium with the surrounding lattice is known as a *polaron*. The lattice oscillations which are important in this problem are not the phonons, but the longitudinal vibrations, in which the ions move in the opposite direction to the surrounding valence electrons; these are just plasma oscillations, and have, to a good approximation, a constant frequency. The electron is treated as a classical particle interacting with a quantum field. Calculations have been made in the weak coupling limit by Pekar (1946), and in the strong coupling by Lee and associates (1953), while a method which appears to be reasonable in intermediate regions has been used by Feynman (1955). A review of the subject has been given by Allcock (1956), and a general treatment has recently been given by Gross (1959).

There are other types of boson-like excitations, as we have discussed earlier. The method of Sawada (1957) demonstrates the existence of such excitations in systems of fermions, and they are plasmons or phonons of zero sound according to whether the fermoins are charged or neutral. There are also phonons in superfluid systems of fermions (Anderson, 1958), and there may be spin waves in fermion systems (Abrikosov and Khalatnikov, 1959). In liquid helium and in classical liquids there are phonons, and in ferromagnetic and antiferromagnetic substances there are spin waves. From the point of view of quantum mechanics, all these excitations are similar, and their properties can be studied by the same formal techniques.

The theory of interacting bosons is discussed in *The Many-Body Problem* (Methuen, 1959) by Brueckner, Beliaev, and Huang.

References

The chapters and sections in which a reference occurs are given in brackets after the reference.

ABE, R. (1958). *Progr. Theoret. Phys. (Kyoto)* **19**, 1 [9.2].

ABRIKOSOV, A. A. and KHALATNIKOV, I. M. (1959). *Repts. Progr. Phys.* **22**, 329 [5.5, 5.6, 9.3].

ALLCOCK, G. R. (1956). *Advances in Phys.* **5**, 412 [9.3].

AMADO, R. D. (1958). *Phys. Rev.* **111**, 548 [4.7].

ANDERSON, P. W. (1958). *Phys. Rev.* **112**, 1900 [6.4, 6.5, 8.8, 9.3].

ANDERSON, P. W., and MOREL, P. (1960). *Phys. Rev. Letters* **5**, 136 and 282 [6.8].

ATKINS, K. R. (1959). "Liquid Helium," Cambridge Univ. Press, London and New York [9.2].

AVILES, J. B. (1958). *Ann. Physics* **5**, 251 [3.7].

BARDEEN, J. (1956). In "Handbuch der Physik," Vol. XV, pp. 274–369. Springer, Berlin [6.3].

BARDEEN, J., COOPER, L. N., and SCHRIEFFER, J. R. (1957). *Phys. Rev.* **108**, 1175 [6.4, 6.5, 6.7, 7.1, 8.8, 9.2, 9.3].

BARDEEN, J., and SCHRIEFFER, J. R. (1960). "Progress in Low Temperature Physics," Vol. III. North-Holland, Amsterdam, to be published [6.7, 8.8].

BELYAEV, S. T. (1959). *Kgl. Danske Videnskab. Selskab, Mat.-fys. Medd.* **31**, No. 11 [6.9].

BETHE, H. A. (1956). *Phys. Rev.* **103**, 1353 [3.5, 4.1, 4.7, 4.8].

BETHE, H. A., and BACHER, R. F. (1936). *Revs. Modern Phys.* **8**, 82 [3.4].

BETHE, H. A., and GOLDSTONE, J. (1957). *Proc. Roy. Soc.* **A238**, 551 [4.7].

BIONDI, M. A., FORRESTER, A. T., GARFUNKEL, M. P., and SATTERTHWAITE, C. B. (1958). *Revs. Modern Phys.* **30**, 1109 [6.3].

BLOCH, C., and DE DOMINICIS, C. (1958). *Nuclear Phys.* **7**, 459 [7.2].

BLOCH, C., and DE DOMINICIS, C. (1959). *Nuclear Phys.* **10**, 181 [7.2, 7.5].

BLOCH, F. (1928). *Z. Physik* **52**, 555 [6.5].

BOGOLIUBOV, N. N. (1947). *J. Phys. (U.S.S.R.)* **11**, 23 [9.2].

BOGOLIUBOV, N. N., and ZUBAREV, N. (1955). *Zhur. Eksp. i Teoret. Fiz.* **28**, 129: translation in *Soviet Phys. JETP* **1**, 83 (1955) [9.2].

BOGOLIUBOV, N. N., ZUBAREV, D. N., and TSERKOVNIKOV, IU. A. (1957). *Doklady Akad. Nauk S.S.S.R.* **117**, 788: translation in *Soviet Phys. Doklady* **2**, 535 (1958) [6.7].

BOGOLIUBOV, N. N., TOLMACHEV, V. V., and SHIRKOV, D. V. (1959). "A New Method in the Theory of Superconductivity," pp. 31–49. Consultants Bureau, New York [6.5, 8.8].

BOHM, D., and GROSS, E. P. (1949). *Phys. Rev.* **75**, 1851 [8.3].

BOHM, D., and PINES, D. (1953). *Phys. Rev.* **92**, 609 [8.3, 8.6].

BOHR, A., and MOTTELSON, B. R. (1953). *Kgl. Danske Videnskab. Selskab, Mat.-fys. Medd.* **27**, No. 16 [5.7].

BOHR, A., and MOTTELSON, B. R. (1958). *Kgl. Norske Videnskab. Selskab Forh.* **31**, 71 [5.7].

BONCH-BRUEVICH, V. L., and KOGAN, SH. M. (1959). *Fiz. Tverdogo Tela* **1**, 1221 [8.3, 8.5].

BONCH-BRUEVICH, V. L., and KOGAN, SH. M. (1960). *Ann. Physics* **9**, 125 [8.1].

BREWER, D. F., DAUNT, J. G., and SREEDHAR, A. K. (1959). *Phys. Rev.* **115**, 836 [5.5].

BROUT, R. (1957). *Phys. Rev.* **108**, 515 [8.4].

BROWN, G. E. (1959). *Revs. Modern Phys.* **31**, 893 [5.4].

BROWN, G. E., and BOLSTERLI, M. (1959). *Phys. Rev. Letters* **3**, 472 [5.11].

BROWN, G. E. CASTILLEJO, L., and EVANS, J. A. (1961). *Nuclear Phys.* **22**, 1 [5.11].

BRUECKNER, K. A., and GAMMEL, J. L. (1958a). *Phys. Rev.* **109**, 1023 [4.7, 5.4].

BRUECKNER, K. A., and GAMMEL, J. L. (1958b). *Phys. Rev.* **109**, 1040 [4.7].

BRUECKNER, K. A., and GOLDMAN, D. T. (1959). *Phys. Rev.* **116**, 424 [4.8].

BRUECKNER, K. A., and LEVINSON, C. A. (1955). *Phys. Rev.* **97**, 1344 [4.7].

BRUECKNER, K. A., and SAWADA, K. (1957). *Phys. Rev.* **106**, 1117 and 1128 [9.2].

BRUECKNER, K. A., and WADA, W. (1956). *Phys. Rev.* **103**, 1008 [4.7].

BRUECKNER, K. A., and WATSON, K. M. (1953). *Phys. Rev.* **92**, 1023 [4.7].

BRUECKNER, K. A., LEVINSON, C. A., and MAHMOUD, H. M. (1954). *Phys. Rev.* **95**, 217 [4.7].

BRUECKNER, K. A., EDEN, R. J., and FRANCIS, N. C. (1955). *Phys. Rev.* **98**, 1445 [4.7].

BRUECKNER, K. A., GAMMEL, J. L., and WEITZNER, H. (1958). *Phys. Rev.* **110**, 431 [4.8].

BRUECKNER, K. A., GAMMEL, J. L., and KUBIS, J. T. (1960a). *Phys. Rev.* **118**, 1438 [4.8, 5.4].

BRUECKNER, K. A., SODA, T., ANDERSON, P. W., and MOREL, P. (1960b). *Phys. Rev.* **118**, 1442 [6.8].

BRUECKNER, K. A., LOCKETT, A. M., and ROTENBERG, M. (1961). *Phys. Rev.* **121**, 255 [4.8].

CHEN, C. (1959). *Doklady Akad. Nauk (S.S.S.R.)* **125**, 1238: translation in: *Soviet Phys. Doklady* **4**, 413 [8.6].

DABROWSKI, J. (1958). *Bull. acad. polon. sci. (Classe III)* **6**, 635 [3.7].

DEBYE, P., and HÜCKEL, E. (1923). *Physik. Z.* **24**, 185 [8.4, 8.5].

DE DOMINICIS, C. T. (1957). University of Birmingham Ph.D. thesis (unpublished) [4.9].

DE-SHALIT, A., and WEISSKOPF, V. F. (1958). *Ann. Physics* **5**, 282 [4.7].

DIRAC, P. A. M. (1930). *Proc. Cambridge Phil. Soc.* **26**, 376 [5.10].

DUBOIS, D. F. (1959). *Ann. Physics* **7**, 174; **8**, 24 [8.4].

DYSON, F. J. (1949a). *Phys. Rev.* **75**, 486 [4.2].

DYSON, F. J. (1949b). *Phys. Rev.* **75**, 1736 [5.3].

DYSON, F. J. (1957). *Phys. Rev.* **106**, 20 [9.2].

EDEN, R. J., EMERY, V. J., and SAMPANTHAR, S. (1959). *Proc. Roy. Soc.* **A253**, 177 and 186 [4.8].

EHRENREICH, H., and COHEN, M. H. (1959). *Phys. Rev.* **115**, 786 [5.10].

EINSTEIN, A. (1924). *Sitzber. preuss. Akad. Wiss., Physik.-math. Kl.* p. 261 (6.2).

EINSTEIN, A. (1925). *Sitzber. preuss. Akad. Wiss., Physik.-math. Kl.* p. 3 [6.2].

ELLIOTT, J. P., and SKYRME, T. H. R. (1955). *Proc. Roy. Soc.* **A232**, 561 [2.4, 5.7].

EMERY, V. J., and SESSLER, A. M. (1960). *Phys. Rev.* **119**, 43 [6.8].

EULER, H. (1937). *Z. Physik* **105**, 553 [3.5].

FAIRBANK, W. M., BUCKINGHAM, M. J., and KELLERS, C. F. (1958). *Proc. 5th Intern. Conf. Low Temperature Phys. & Chem.* p. 50. Univ. of Wisconsin, Madison, Wisconsin [6.2].

FERNBACH, S., SERBER, R., and TAYLOR, T. B. (1949). *Phys. Rev.* **75**, 1352 [3.8].

FERRELL, R. A. (1957). *Phys. Rev.* **107**, 1631 [5.10].

FERRELL, R. A. (1958). *Phys. Rev. Letters* **1**, 443 [8.4].

FESHBACH, H., PORTER, C. E., and WEISSKOPF, V. F. (1954). *Phys. Rev.* **96**, 448 [3.8].

FEYNMAN, R. P. (1949). *Phys. Rev.* **76**, 769 [4.2].

FEYNMAN, R. P. (1953). *Phys. Rev.* **91**, 1301 [9.2].

FEYNMAN, R. P. (1954). *Phys. Rev.* **94**, 262 [9.2].

FEYNMAN, R. P. (1955). *Phys. Rev.* **97**, 660 [9.3].

FEYNMAN, R. P. (1957). *Revs. Modern Phys.* **29**, 205 [6.3].

FEYNMAN, R. P., and COHEN, M. (1956). *Phys. Rev.* **102**, 1189 [9.2].

FOCK, V. I. (1930). *Z. Physik* **61**, 126 [3.2].

FRANCIS, N. C., and WATSON, K. M. (1953). *Phys. Rev.* **92**, 291 [4.7].

FRENKEL, J. (1934). "Wave Mechanics: Advanced General Theory," pp. 435–439. Oxford Univ. Press, London and New York [5.10].

FRÖHLICH, H. (1950). *Phys. Rev.* **79**, 845 [6.3, 6.5, 9.3].

GALITSKII, V. M., and MIGDAL, A. B. (1958). *Zhur. Eksp. i Teoret. Fiz.* **34**, 139; translation in: *Soviet Phys. JETP* **7**, 96 [5.2].

GARTENHAUS, S., and SCHWARTZ, C. (1957). *Phys. Rev.* **108**, 482 [2.4].

GELL-MANN, M. (1957). *Phys. Rev.* **106**, 369 [8.4].

GELL-MANN, M., and BRUECKNER, K. A. (1957). *Phys. Rev.* **106**, 364 [8.4].

GLASSGOLD, A. E. (1959). In "Progress in Nuclear Physics," Vol. 7, p. 123. Pergamon, London [3.8].

GOLDHABER, M., and TELLER, E. (1948). *Phys. Rev.* **74**, 1046 [5.7, 5.11].

GOLDSTONE, J. (1957). *Proc. Roy. Soc.* **A239**, 267 [4.2, 4.6, 4.7].

GOLDSTONE, J., and GOTTFRIED, K. (1959). *Nuovo cimento* [10] **13**, 849 [5.10].

GOMBÁS, P. (1949). "Die statistische Theorie des Atoms und ihre Anwendungen." Springer, Vienna [3.3].

GOMBÁS, P. (1952a). *Acta Phys. Hungarica* **1**, 329 [3.4].

GOMBÁS, P. (1952b). *Acta Phys. Hungarica* **2**, 223 [3.4].

GOMBÁS, P., MÁGORI, E., MOLNÁR, B., and SZABÓ, E. (1955). *Acta Phys. Hungarica* **4**, 267 [3.4].

GOMBAS, P., SZEPFALUSY, P., and MÁGORI, E. (1957). *Acta Phys. Hungarica* **7**, 223 [3.4].

GOMES, L. C., WALECKA, J. D., and WEISSKOPF, V. F. (1958). *Ann. Physics* **3**, 241 [4.7].

GREEN, A. E. S. (1958). *Revs. Modern Phys.* **30**, 569 [3.4].

GRIFFIN, J. J., and RICH, M. (1960). *Phys. Rev.* **118**, 850 [5.8].

GRIFFIN, J. J., and WHEELER, J. A. (1957). *Phys. Rev.* **108**, 311 [5.8].

GROSS, E. P. (1959). *Ann. Physics* **8**, 78 [9.3].

GROSS, E. P. (1960a). *Phys. Rev. Letters* **4**, 599 [3.6].

GROSS, E. P. (1960b). *Nuclear Phys.* **14**, 389 [5.8].

GROSS, E. P. (1960c). *Ann. Physics* **9**, 292 [9.2].

HARTREE, D. R. (1928). *Proc. Cambridge Phil. Soc.* **24**, 89 [3.2].

HARTREE, D. R. (1957). "The Calculation of Atomic Structures." Wiley, New York [3.2].

HILL, D. L., and WHEELER, J. A. (1953). *Phys. Rev.* **89**, 1102 [5.8]

HOFSTADTER, R. (1956). *Revs. Modern Phys.* **28**, 214 [3.4].

HUANG, K. (1960). *Phys. Rev.* **119**, 1129 [9.2].

HUANG, K., and YANG, C. N. (1957). *Phys. Rev.* **105**, 767 [9.2].

HUBBARD, J. (1957). *Proc. Roy. Soc.* **A240**, 539 [8.6].

HUBBARD, J. (1958). *Proc. Roy. Soc.* **A243**, 336 [8.6].

HUBY, R. (1949). *Proc. Phys. Soc. (London)* **A62**, 62 [3.5].

HUGENHOLTZ, N. M. (1957). *Physica* **23**, 481 [4.2, 4.4, 4.7, 5.4].

HUGENHOLTZ, N. M., and PINES, D. (1959). *Phys. Rev.* **116**, 489 [9.2].

HUGENHOLTZ, N. M., and VAN HOVE, L. (1958). *Physica* **24**, 363 [4.8].

INGLIS, D. R. (1954). *Phys. Rev.* **96**, 1059 [5.8].

INGLIS, D. R. (1956). *Phys. Rev.* **103**, 1786 [5.8].

IWAMOTO, F., and YAMADA, M. (1957). *Progr. Theoret. Phys. (Kyoto)* **18**, 345 [3.7].

JASTROW, R. (1955). *Phys. Rev.* **98**, 1479 [3.7].

KADANOFF, L. P., and MARTIN, P. C. (1960). *Phys. Rev.* To be published [8.6].

KAHN, B., and UHLENBECK, G. E. (1938). *Physica* **5**, 399 [7.5].

KINOSHITA, T., and NAMBU, Y. (1954). *Phys. Rev.* **94**, 598 [8.4].

KOHN, W., and LUTTINGER, J. M. (1960). *Phys. Rev.* **118**, 41 [7.3].

KUBO, R. (1956). *Can. J. Phys.* **34**, 1274 [8.7].

LANDAU, L. D. (1941). *J. Phys. (U.S.S.R.)* **5**, 71 [9.2].

LANDAU, L. D. (1956). *Zhur. Eksp. i Teoret. Fiz.* **30**, 1058; translation in: *Soviet Phys. JETP* **3**, 920 [5.5].

LANDAU, L. D. (1958). *Zhur. Eksp. i Teoret. Fiz.* **35**, 97; translation in: *Soviet Phys. JETP* **8**, 70. [5.9].

168   REFERENCES

LANGMUIR, I., and TONKS, L. (1929). *Phys. Rev.* **33**, 195 [8.3]

LAQUER, H. L., SYDORIAK, S. G., and ROBERTS, T. R. (1959). *Phys. Rev.* **113**, 417 [5.6].

LEE, T. D., and YANG, C. N. (1959a). *Phys. Rev.* **113**, 1165 [7.5, 9.2].

LEE, T. D., and YANG, C. N. (1959b). *Phys. Rev.* **116**, 25 [9.2].

LEE, T. D., and YANG, C. N. (1960). *Phys. Rev.* **117**, 12, 22 and 897 [9.2].

LEE, T. D., LOW, F. E., and PINES, D. (1953). *Phys. Rev.* **90**, 297 [9.3].

LEE, T. D., HUANG, K., and YANG, C. N. (1957). *Phys. Rev.* **106**, 1135 [9.2].

LEVINGER, J. S., and BETHE, H. A. (1950). *Phys. Rev.* **78**, 115 [5.11].

LONDON, F. (1938). *Phys. Rev.* **54**, 947 [6.2].

LÖWDIN, P.-O. (1955). *Phys. Rev.* **97**, 1474 [2.2].

LUTTINGER, J. M., and WARD, J. C. (1960). *Phys. Rev.* **118**, 1417 [7.3].

MARCH, N. H. (1957). *Advances in Phys.* **6**, 1 [3.3].

MARTIN, P. C., and SCHWINGER, J. (1959). *Phys. Rev.* **115**, 1342 [8.1, 8.6].

MATSUBARA, T. (1955). *Progr. Theoret. Phys. (Kyoto)* **14**, 351 [7.2, 9.2].

MAXWELL, E. (1950). *Phys. Rev.* **78**, 477 [6.3].

MAYER, J. (1937). *J. Chem. Phys.* **5**, 67 [7.5].

MAYER, M. G. (1950). *Phys. Rev.* **78**, 22 [6.9].

MAYER, M. G., and JENSEN, J. H. D. (1955). "Elementary Theory of Nuclear Shell Structure." Wiley, New York [3.8].

MILLS, R. L., SESSLER, A. M., MOSZKOWSKI, S. A., and SHANKLAND, D. G. (1959). *Phys. Rev. Letters* **3**, 381 [6.9].

MONTROLL, E. W., and WARD, J. C. (1958). *Phys. Fluids* **1**, 55 [7.2, 8.3, 8.4].

OVERHAUSER, A. W. (1960). *Phys. Rev. Letters* **4**, 415 [3.6].

PEIERLS, R. E. (1938). *Phys. Rev.* **54**, 918 [6.6].

PEIERLS, R. E., and YOCCOZ, J. (1957). *Proc. Phys. Soc. (London)* **A70**, 381 [5.8].

PEKAR, S. I. (1946). *J. Phys. (U.S.S.R.)* **10**, 341 [9.3].

PINES, D. (1953). *Phys. Rev.* **92**, 626 [8.3].

PINES, D. (1958). *Phys. Rev.* **109**, 280 [6.5].

PRANGE, R. E., and KLEIN, A. B. (1958). *Phys. Rev.* **112**, 994 [5.3].

RACAH, G. (1949). *Phys. Rev.* **76**, 1352 [6.4].

REYNOLDS, C. A., SERIN, B., WRIGHT, W. H., and NESBITT, L. B. (1950). *Phys. Rev.* **78**, 487 [6.3].

SACHS, R. G., and AUSTERN, N. (1951). *Phys. Rev.* **81**, 705 [5.11].

SALPETER, E. E. (1958). *Ann. Physics* **5**, 183 [7.5].

SAWADA, K. (1957). *Phys. Rev.* **106**, 372 [8.4, 8.6, 9.3].

SAWADA, K., BRUECKNER, K. A., FUKUDA, N., and BROUT, R. (1957). *Phys. Rev.* **108**, 507 [8.3, 8.4].

SCHULTZ, T. D. (1958). *Nuovo cimento* [10] **8**, 943 [6.6].

SERIN, B. (1956). In "Handbuch der Physik," Vol. XV, pp. 210–73. Springer, Berlin [6.3].

SHAW, G. L. (1959). *Ann. Physics* **8**, 509 [5.4].

SKYRME, T. H. R. (1959). *Nuclear Phys.* **9**, 615 [5.11].

SWIATECKI, W. J. (1951). *Proc. Phys. Soc. (London)* **A64**, 226 [3.4].

SWIATECKI, W. J. (1956). *Phys. Rev.* **103**, 265 [4.7].

SWIATECKI, W. J. (1957). Proceedings of the Pittsburgh Conference on Nuclear Structure, pp. 173–88. (unpublished) [3.4].

TEMMER, G. M. (1958). *Revs. Modern Phys.* **30**, 498 [3.8].

THOULESS, D. J. (1957). *Phys. Rev.* **107**, 559 [4.7].

THOULESS, D. J. (1958). *Phys. Rev.* **112**, 906 [4.7, 4.8].

THOULESS, D. J. (1959). *Phys. Rev.* **114**, 1383 [5.3, 5.4].

THOULESS, D. J. (1960). *Phys. Rev.* **117**, 1256 [6.4].

TOMONAGA, S. (1955a). *Progr. Theoret. Phys. (Kyoto)* **13**, 467 [5.7].

TOMONAGA, S. (1955b). *Progr. Theoret. Phys. (Kyoto)* **13**, 482 [8.6].

VALATIN, J. G. (1958). *Nuovo cimento* [10] **7**, 843 [6.7].

VALATIN, J. G., and BUTLER, D. (1958). *Nuovo cimento* [10] **10**, 37 [9.2].

VAN HOVE, L. (1960). *Physica,* **26**, S 200 [4.4].

WADA, Y., TAKANO, F., and FUKUDA, N. (1958). *Progr. Theoret. Phys. (Kyoto)* **19**, 597 [6.4, 6.5].

WATSON, K. M. (1953). *Phys. Rev.* **89**, 575 [4.7].

WATSON, K. M. (1957). *Phys. Rev.* **105**, 1388 [4.7].

WICK, G. C. (1950). *Phys. Rev.* **80**, 268 [4.3].

WIGNER, E. P. (1934). *Phys. Rev.* **46**, 1002 [8.4].

WILETS, L. (1958). *Revs. Modern Phys.* **30**, 542 [3.4].

WILKINSON, D. H. (1956). *Physica* **22**, 1039 [5.11].

YOCCOZ, J. (1957). *Proc. Phys. Soc. (London)* **A70**, 388 [5.8].

ZYRIANOV, P. S., and ELEONSKII, V. M. (1956). *Zhur. Eksp. i Teoret. Fiz.* **30**, 592; translation in: *Soviet Phys. JETP* **3**, 620 [5.10].

INDEX

171